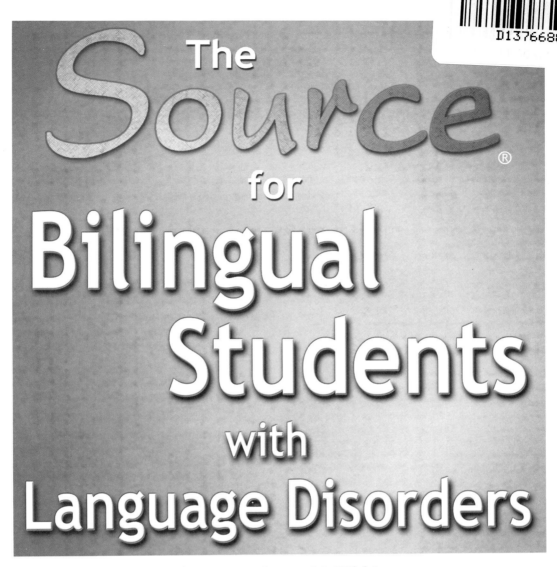

The Source for Bilingual Students with Language Disorders

Celeste Roseberry-McKibbin

Skill:	Bilingual Language
Ages:	5 and up
Grades:	K and up

LinguiSystems

LinguiSystems, Inc.
3100 4th Avenue
East Moline, IL 61244

800-776-4332

FAX: 800-577-4555
E-mail: service@linguisystems.com
Web: linguisystems.com

GOVERNORS STATE UNIVERSITY
UNIVERSITY PARK
IL 60466

Printed in the U.S.A.
ISBN 10: 0-7606-0332-4
ISBN 13: 978-0-7606-0332-1

About the Author

Celeste Roseberry-McKibbin received her Ph.D. from Northwestern University. She is an Associate Professor of Speech Pathology and Audiology at California State University, Sacramento. Dr. Roseberry is also currently a part-time itinerant speech pathologist in Elk Grove Unified School District where she provides direct services to elementary students. She has worked in educational and medical settings with a wide variety of clients ranging from preschoolers through geriatric patients.

Dr. Roseberry's primary research interests are in the areas of assessment and treatment of multicultural students with communication disorders as well as language skills of children from low-income backgrounds. She has over 30 publication credits, including several books, and has made over 100 presentations at the local, state, and national levels. She lived in the Philippines from ages 6 to 17.

The Source for Bilingual Students with Language Disorders is Celeste's first publication with LinguiSystems.

Dedication

To my parents, Floyd and Beverly Roseberry

Thank you for giving me life and for your continued presence in my life and heart.

Table of Contents

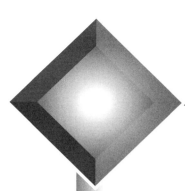

Introduction

In the U.S. today, many speech-language pathologists (SLPs) are finding themselves serving increasing numbers of bilingual students in the public schools. When these students are placed into speech-language therapy because they have underlying language-learning disabilities (LLD), they need to receive treatment that will adequately address their needs and improve their language skills for academic and social success.

Research indicates that ideally, students who are English language learners should receive treatment in their primary language. However, there are two realities that prevent this:

1. Most SLPs speak only English.

2. Students on a caseload may represent a variety of language backgrounds. For example, one English-speaking SLP's caseload may include Punjabi, Hispanic, Vietnamese, Russian, and Laotian students.

Because of these realities, most SLPs end up conducting therapy in English. Yet, these SLPs are plagued with doubts about how to best go about this. Many questions come to mind. What do these bilingual students with LLD need the most? Where do I begin? What are priorities in treatment? How can I successfully teach a student when he or she is a limited speaker of English and I don't speak his or her primary language? How is therapy for a bilingual student different from therapy with a monolingual, English-speaking student?

The need for answers to these questions is pressing. The primary answer is both deceptively simple and enormously complex: these students need treatment that best combines approaches and principles from the fields of speech-language pathology and second-language acquisition. SLPs who work with these students ideally provide a combination of language therapy and English as a second language (ESL) teaching.

However, there are four major obstacles to providing this kind of ideal therapy. First, most SLPs do not have a background in ESL or second-language acquisition and most SLPs do not know basic principles of second language learning. However, knowledge and application of these principles is essential for successful treatment of bilingual students with LLD. Second, the vast majority of SLPs do not have time to take classes and read books which will provide them with this essential knowledge. Third, there are virtually no materials in the field of speech-language pathology that provide clinicians with convenient, time-saving, appropriate materials for use in therapy with bilingual LLD students. A fourth problem faced by many clinicians is that therapy in the schools is often sporadic and conducted with large groups of students. Thus, SLPs may present concepts, but interruptions in therapy and large groups prevent optimal learning from taking place. Many SLPs feel frustrated with this situation.

The purpose of this book is to provide a practical, useable, convenient source for SLPs who are faced with the dilemma above. The book targets beginning through intermediate bilingual LLD students in grades K-8. Students of different ages have such unique profiles that the book is designed to be extremely flexible for each individual clinician's caseload. For example, some objectives and activities may be most appropriate for Student A, a Spanish-speaking second grader born in the U.S. with some prior exposure to English. Other objectives and activities will be best for Student B, a seventh grade Vietnamese refugee who has been in the U.S. for one month and has spent most of her life in Southeast Asian refugee camps. The activities, strategies, and stimuli are designed to accommodate each of these students depending upon the individual clinician's judgment.

This book has two major goals:

➤ **The first goal of the book** is to teach English vocabulary to bilingual LLD students. Although these students have many pressing needs, none is greater than the learning of English vocabulary. Each chapter has measurable objectives for teaching English vocabulary to students. Grammar (syntax and morphology) is not explicitly taught because for beginning English learners, vocabulary is a much higher priority. Literature in second-language acquisition shows that most second language learners are not ready to work on details of grammar until they have been exposed to the new language for at least 1-2 years. However, these learners can certainly benefit from hearing grammatically correct second language structures modeled by the clinician.

➤ **The second goal of the book**, besides helping clinicians teach English vocabulary to English language learners (ELLs) with LLD, is to provide objectives and activities which target phonological awareness skills. Many ELL LLD students are nonliterate in their primary languages, and thus do not come to school with a foundation of literacy. This alone is a true barrier for them in terms of learning reading, writing, and spelling in a second language. These students have the additional challenge of attempting to become literate in an unfamiliar language when they have an underlying language-learning system that causes them to have intrinsic learning difficulties. Because of these two major barriers, many ELL LLD students struggle greatly with English literacy.

Although many SLPs do not regard teaching literacy skills as within their job descriptions, it is necessary for SLPs to be involved in helping all LLD students with the language of literacy (Dodge, 2000). This is best done by helping students develop foundational phonological awareness skills, which serve as the basis for all other literacy skills such as reading, writing, and spelling. Phonological awareness skills are especially crucial for ELL LLD students.

The activities and materials within this book target primarily vocabulary (semantics) and phonological awareness skills in a direct, objective, measurable manner. IEP goals and objectives are included in every vocabulary unit. These can be directly used to satisfy the requirements of the Individuals with Disabilities Education Act (IDEA, 1997). However, other skills are indirectly addressed. These skills include auditory processing (especially auditory memory), reading, writing, spelling, syntax, morphology, and pragmatics. These skills are not directly targeted or measured, but rather are interwoven into activities targeting development of vocabulary and phonological awareness skills.

A unique feature of the book is that vocabulary words are presented a minimum of 10 times. The words are reviewed repeatedly. A problem with many available treatment materials is that vocabulary words are presented 1-2 times and not reviewed again. Thus, if one student in a group of 5 is absent on Monday when the words are presented for the first time, he "misses" those words and is behind the other 4 students when the group is seen again on Wednesday. Also, LLD students are notorious for needing multiple exemplars and repetitions of concepts in order to truly master these concepts. When these LLD students are learning the words in a second language, the need for repeated exposure to the words becomes even more urgent. The Thematic Redundance approach, upon which this book is based, gives students these necessary repeated exposures to new vocabulary words.

In the Thematic Redundance approach, the focus is on vocabulary learning. However, the approach acknowledges that ELL students with LLD need support in other areas as well. Using the vocabulary words in Units 1-7, clinicians can use activities to work on other skill areas. As stated, these skill areas include auditory processing (especially auditory memory), reading, writing, spelling, syntax, morphology, and pragmatics. Again, the emphasis is upon learning vocabulary through multiple exposures to each word through different kinds of activities. The activities help promote redundance of the vocabulary and thus greater retention of the words learned. Emphasis is placed upon helping students develop vocabulary and skills that will promote social success as well as success in the regular education classroom.

The Thematic Redundance approach uses principles of teaching English as a second language as well as successful strategies for students with LLD. This book is geared toward combining the best current theory and practice in the fields of second-language acquisition and speech-language pathology to help ELL students with LLD develop their English vocabulary as well as skills in other areas. To this end, activities and materials in both sections of the book (described in more detail on the next page) are based generally on the following hierarchy of second-language acquisition:

Stage I—Preproduction

➤ Students focus on listening and comprehension.

➤ Students are allowed not to speak until they are comfortable.

➤ Activities involve opportunities for responding in nonverbal ways such as pointing.

Stage II—Early Production

➤ Students are gradually encouraged to give short responses (e.g., 1-3 words).

➤ The SLP continues to emphasize comprehension of English.

➤ There is no overt correction of grammatical errors in English; correct patterns are modeled but students are not corrected.

Stage III—Speech Emergence

➤ Students may use English stock phrases and patterns such as simple sentences modeled by the SLP.

➤ Students may generate simple sentences.

➤ Students may begin to interact with others in English.

Stage IV—Intermediate Fluency

➤ Students engage more in conversation and interaction with others.

➤ Students produce simple connected oral narratives.

➤ Students refine their grammatical skills, although there is still no overt correction of grammatical errors (modeling of correct structures continues).

➤ Students engage in basic literacy activities in English.

A very attractive feature of this book is that the preparation is done for the clinician. The reproducible treatment activities are so straightforward that no planning time is required. In addition, an SLP who works with a paraprofessional or aide can easily have the aide carry out the activities with groups of children. This author found, as a public school SLP with an aide, that one notable disadvantage of having an aide was that it took a lot of time to explain the treatment activities to the aide. It almost took more time than seeing the children personally. The activities in this book can be given to an aide and he or she can successfully carry out the activities with virtually no explanation necessary.

Another attractive feature of this book is that clinicians can easily, quickly, and directly obtain pretest and posttest measures of children's vocabulary and can measure progress

8

quantitatively. Local, state, and federal laws and policies are increasingly demanding data-based measures of treatment progress, and this book allows clinicians to provide these measures with little extra time or work.

The book is designed to be used as follows:

Part 1

1. Part 1 begins with a collection of Teaching Style Strategies (pages 11-13). These strategies can be used in speech-language small group pullout situations as well as in regular education classrooms to promote learning for ELL students with LLD.

2. Beginning on page 14 are specific Treatment Strategies that can be used to help students learn vocabulary in Units 1-7 as well as to build skills in other areas mentioned. These are primarily intervention activities that have been shown to be successful with English language learners; the activities have been modified for use with ELLs with LLD. The intervention strategies are designed to be used sequentially from early through intermediate stages of learning English. For example, the early activities require little speaking on the part of the students; the later activities incorporate basic literacy skills.

Part 2

In Part 2, vocabulary Units 1-7 are presented. Each unit is thematically organized, with 17-20 new words per unit.

Each unit is comprised of five parts:
1. Pre-written IEP objectives/benchmarks with examples of each
2. A pretest, which measures children's initial knowledge of target vocabulary words for that chapter
3. Pictures of target vocabulary words
4. Small cards with each target word written out in print
5. Several pages of reproducible treatment activities

Summary
This book is designed to help SLPs serve LLD students who are learning English as a second language. The book is a practical therapy tool which focuses on developing vocabulary and phonological awareness skills. Other skill areas are also indirectly targeted. It is the author's hope that SLPs who serve ELL LLD students will find the book to be a valuable, practical, time-saving resource that will truly support the success of all ELL LLD students.

9

Part 1

Teaching Style Strategies

Best Practices for English Language Learners with Language-Learning Disabilities

Introduction

Speech-language pathologists, teachers, and other professionals need to modify their style of teaching and their overall interaction with English language learners (ELLs) who also have language-learning disabilities (LLD). These students have a dual challenge. They are trying to learn a second language with an underlying language-learning system that is inadequate for even learning one language.

The following suggestions can be used in small pullout therapy groups, regular education classrooms, and any other settings in which there are students who are English learners with LLD (Roseberry-McKibbin, 1995). Speech-language pathologists can reproduce these suggestions for other professionals and team members who serve ELL LLD students.

Specific Teaching Style Strategies

➤ Remember that students of all ages who are in the early stages of English language learning may speak little if they speak at all. Many learners, when they are first exposed to a second language, go through a "silent period" where they are focusing on comprehension of the second language. The silent period may last from several weeks to 1-2 years. The younger the ELL student, the longer the silent period tends to last. It is not uncommon for preschoolers, for example, to have a silent period that lasts for 1-2 years (Tabors, 1997).

➤ Because of this silent period, it is crucial to initially focus on comprehension activities with little emphasis on production. ELL students with LLD should never be forced to speak if they are not comfortable or ready. This is a major difference between intervention with monolingual and bilingual LLD students: with monolingual LLD students, production is emphasized immediately. With ELL students with LLD, clinicians and teachers can gently encourage production while respecting the fact that it might be several months or more before the student is ready to actually speak in English.

➤ When speaking to ELL students with LLD, it is critical to slow down the rate of speech. When teachers and clinicians speak more slowly, these students can process information more effectively. Remember—there is an underlying language-learning disability which makes it difficult to process incoming auditory information at a normal rate. And, the student is attempting to accomplish this challenging task in an unfamiliar language.

➤ Pause often. Pauses give the student time to process the information. Pauses can occur initially between words, and then between phrases, and eventually between longer linguistic units such as sentences.

➤ Use shorter sentences. Pause in between these sentences. Lengthy sentences are very difficult for ELL LLD students to process.

➤ In the early stages, use fewer polysyllabic words. Monosyllabic, simple words are easier for beginning ELL LLD learners to process.

➤ Many clinicians and teachers tend to state information quickly and only once. It is important to repeat, rephrase, and restate information. For example, the clinician can say, "Grapes are a fruit. They can be green or purple. They taste good. Green and purple grapes are fruit. Grapes taste good!"

➤ Use a multimodal approach to learning. ELL students with LLD benefit tremendously from seeing, hearing, and touching. A multisensory approach, where students learn in a hands-on manner, will promote the fastest, most effective learning for ELL LLD students. Many learn well kinesthetically and benefit from the incorporation of bodily movement into activities whenever possible. For example, if students draw or write about new words they have learned, they will remember these words better later. Auditory information can be supplemented with visuals such as charts, pictures, objects, and overheads.

➤ Before beginning a class, therapy session, or activity, use preparatory sets to inform students what is about to happen. For example, the clinician can say, "Today we are going to start learning about safety words. We will look at pictures, read the words, and then color the pictures. So, today, we will talk about safety words and look at pictures, read words, and then color." When the students hear redundant preparatory sets or lead statements such as the ones above, they will learn new information more readily.

➤ Allow extra processing time after answering questions. It is recommended that after asking a question of an ELL student with LLD, the clinician allow at least 3 seconds for the student to answer.

➤ Try to teach new information in as quiet an atmosphere as possible. Because many of these students have underlying auditory processing difficulties and are also processing new information in an unfamiliar language, they learn best in a quiet atmosphere.

➤ When presenting information, use additional gestures and facial expressions to supplement information by making it more redundant for students.

➤ Use students' names to obtain their attention. For example, the clinician can say, "Phong, what does the word *calendar* mean?"

➤ With students who are in the early stages of learning English, be careful to avoid using idioms or slang. For example, these students will not understand an expression like "Look outside! It's raining cats and dogs! No recess today."

➤ Emphasize key words through slightly exaggerated intonation and increased volume. This will help students focus on the most auditorially salient information. For example, the clinician can say:

> "We are studying **clothes** today. There are **many kinds** of clothes. **Some** are for **women**, and **some** are for **men**. There are **some kinds** of **clothes** that **both men** and **women wear**."

➤ Seat ELL LLD students near the front of the classroom where they can see and hear the teacher easily.

➤ There is some anecdotal evidence that ELL LLD students in classroom settings learn information better if the teacher's voice is 20-30 dB louder than normal. Thus, in classrooms, instructors can use amplifiers to increase the salience of the auditory information and to help students focus on this information more effectively.

➤ Consider assigning a "peer buddy" to ELL LLD students. This can be a classmate or an older student who can give these students extra assistance with tasks in the therapy setting and in the classroom.

13

Treatment Strategy 1: Terrific Techniques

Background & Rationale Many clinicians are familiar with language treatment techniques that are successful with monolingual children with LLD. The following language treatment techniques are highly recommended for LLD students who are in the early through intermediate stages of learning English. These techniques are especially effective because they stimulate language without pressuring the ELL student to produce specific structures.

Technique 1: Focused Stimulation

This technique is ideal for students who are reluctant to speak in the early stages of learning English. The clinician repeatedly models a target structure or vocabulary word during activities designed to focus on the target. For example, if the clinician is teaching the word *pencil* (Unit 1), he or she uses various stimulus materials, discusses them, and says the word *pencil* repeatedly. For example:

Clinician: Look, here is a picture of a *pencil*. The *pencil* is sharp and there is an eraser at the top. You can sharpen a *pencil* before you write with it. Let's see if we can find a *pencil* in this container. Here's a *pencil*! The *pencil* is long, yellow, and skinny. Is there another *pencil* in the container?

Technique 2: Expansion

In expansion, the clinician takes the student's utterances and expands them by adding correct grammatical information. For example:

Student: I see cat meow.
Clinician: Yes, I see the cat meowing.
Student: Cat big.
Clinician: The cat is big.

Technique 3: Extension[1]

In extension, the clinician comments on the child's utterances and adds new semantic information. For example:

Student: This a picture of hot dog.
Clinician: Right—this is a picture of a delicious hot dog with mustard on it.
Student: Here's a hamburger.
Clinician: It looks like this hamburger has lettuce and tomatoes on it.

[1] *adapted from Roseberry-McKibbin & Hegde, 2000*

Background & Rationale Students with LLD who are also learning English need multiple exposures to new target vocabulary words. Using themes is an ideal way to provide these multiple exposures. Students also learn best through repetition and through different sensory-motor activities which help them learn vocabulary through different modalities. Each unit in this book can be enhanced through additional activities which use different activities to help build knowledge of vocabulary words in the different theme or content areas. Also, the students will benefit because they will learn to categorize the information they are learning.

Ideas for Expanding Vocabulary in Each Thematic Unit

➤ Read books which expand upon the themes in each unit. For example, to expand Unit 3 (Food Items), read books or stories that discuss food, restaurants, etc.

➤ Use songs and poems about the theme for each unit. For example, when teaching Unit 2 (Body Parts), sing the "Hokey Pokey" and label body parts during the song.

➤ Use "Simon Says" to have students touch pictures of vocabulary words from that particular unit. Or, words from various units might be combined. For example, the clinician might say, "Simon says touch the lion, tiger, comb, and dress."

➤ Use pantomime to act out a vocabulary word and have the students guess what word it is. The clinician and students can take turns pantomiming the words for the rest of the group to guess.

➤ Have the students write stories using the words they have learned. Students who don't write can draw pictures integrating the new vocabulary words. For example, during the study of Unit 5 (Animals), students could draw a picture of a farm and a zoo and draw the animals they have been learning about.

➤ Use a wall chart (illustrated on the following page) with pockets or slots where students can place vocabulary picture cards according to category.

Wall Chart

Unit 1	Unit 2	Unit 3	Unit 4	Unit 5	Unit 6	Unit 7
School Items	Body Parts	Food Items	Self-Care Items	Animals	Time & Weather	Safety & Survival

Have students place vocabulary picture cards in these pockets.

Treatment Strategy 3: Using Total Physical Response (TPR)

Background & Rationale TPR is an excellent technique for students who are beginning English learners. If they are going through a silent period where they are comprehending but not yet producing English, this method is especially beneficial in learning new words without pressure to produce language too early. In addition, body movement helps to form stronger associations between words and their referents.

Example 1 (Unit 2: Body Parts)

Clinician: Touch your nose. *(Clinician touches her nose.)*

Clinician: Touch your nose. *(Clinician and students all touch their noses.)*

Clinician: Touch your nose. *(Students only—not clinician—touch their noses.)*

Clinician: Touch your nose and eyes. *(Clinician touches his nose and eyes.)*

Clinician: Touch your nose and eyes. *(Clinician and students all touch their noses and eyes.)*

Clinician: Touch your nose and eyes. *(Students only—not clinician—touch their noses and eyes.)*

Example 2 (Unit 3: Food Items)

Clinician: Pick up the grapes, apple, and ice cream. *(Clinician picks up pictures of the grapes, apple, and ice cream.)*

Clinician: Pick up the grapes, apple, and ice cream. *(Clinician and students all pick up pictures of the grapes, apple, and ice cream.)*

Clinician: Pick up the grapes, apple, and ice cream. *(Students only—not clinician—pick up pictures of the grapes, apple, and ice cream.)*

Sources: Asher, 1977; Richards & Rodgers, 1986; Terrell, 1992)

Treatment Strategy 4: KWL Charts

Background & Rationale ELL students with LLD need to become actively involved in the learning process. In addition, it is important for clinicians to build on these students' previous knowledge about any given topic. When students discuss what they already know, decide what they would like to learn, and then list what they learned, they become actively involved and retain information better. KWL charts can be used for any topic area.

Example (Unit 7: Safety and Survival)

Clinician: Today we are going to discuss safety. We know it is important to stay safe. But how do we do that? Let's talk about some things that we know already about safety, and then list some things that we want to know about safety. Later, we'll talk about what we've learned. Let's start with Jaime. Jaime, what's one thing you know about being safe?

Jaime: Police help you stay safe.

Clinician: Yes! Let's write that down as something we know. Gloria, what else do we know about safety?

Gloria: That when someone gets hurt, an ambulance comes.

Clinician: Thanks, Gloria. Let's write that down too. How about one more? Yes, Koeta?

Koeta: Don't get in the car with strangers.

Clinician: That's excellent! Anything else? (no response) OK, let's review what we know about safety. We've written that police help you stay safe, that an ambulance comes for hurt people, and that we don't get in the car with strangers. Now let's talk about what we want to learn. What do we want to know? Yes, Jaime?

Jaime: What does *caution* mean?

Clinician: Good question. How about anyone else? Gloria?

Gloria: What do you do if something says *private*?

Clinician: Let's write that down too—that's important.

Know	**W**ant to Know	**L**earned
Police help us stay safe. Ambulances come for hurt people. Don't get in a car with a stranger.	What does *caution* mean? What should you do if something says "private"?	

Sources: Ogle, 1986; Peregoy & Boyle, 1997

As previously stated, it is ideal for ELL students with LLD to learn new concepts by linking them to what they already know. Thus, when beginning to teach a vocabulary unit, the clinician can use semantic clusters to help students link new concepts to those already familiar to them. Semantic clustering helps students learn new information more quickly because they are able to integrate it with familiar information. Clustering can be done orally and is an ideal written activity for students who are working on writing skills. It can be done with students individually or in groups.

Example (Unit 3: Food Items)

Clinician: We are going to talk about foods today. Let's think about some things we already know about foods. When you give me ideas, I am going to write them down. Meuy, what is your favorite food?

Meuy: I like hamburgers.

Clinician: OK! Let's write down hamburgers. We can get those at McDonald's, Burger King, and lots of places. What do you put on hamburgers? Calder?

Calder: I put ketchup, tomatoes, and lettuce on my hamburgers.

Clinician: Let's write those things down too. What other foods do you or your families like to get when you go out? Yes, Ramon?

Ramon: My family likes to get ice cream after we have eaten our hamburgers.

Clinician: Let's write that down! Now—what kinds of fruits do you and your families eat at home? Yes, Dominique?

Dominique: We like grapes and cherries. But they don't have those in the Philippines.

Clinician: That's right. What other fruits or vegetables do you and your families eat at home?

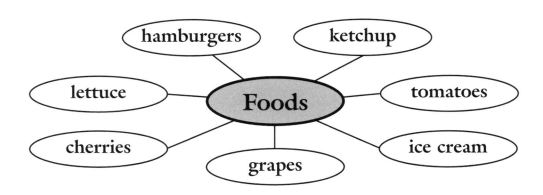

Treatment Strategy 6: Memorable Maps

Background & Rationale   Because ELL students who are LLD have difficulty with categorizing and retrieving specific information about words, semantic maps can be very helpful for these students. Semantic maps also use the powerful strategy of allowing students to tie new knowledge to previous knowledge for more rapid learning. Semantic maps also extend students' mental representations of word meanings.

Example (Unit 5: Animals)

Clinician: We are going to talk about animals in several different ways. We will draw pictures to help us do this. First, we will talk about how they feel. Second, we will talk about how they look. Third, we will talk about what they do. Let's start with a tiger. Who can tell me how a tiger feels? (The clinician then continues generating descriptors of tigers until there are at least 3-4 descriptors per category.)

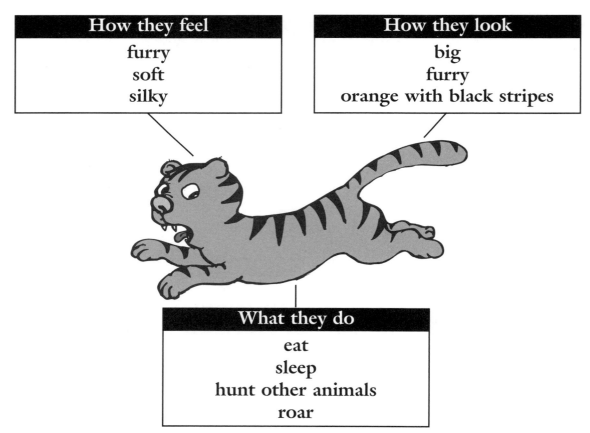

How they feel
furry
soft
silky

How they look
big
furry
orange with black stripes

What they do
eat
sleep
hunt other animals
roar

adapted from Beaumont, 1992

Background & Rationale Students who are ELL and LLD need multiple exemplars of the target concepts that they are learning. Multiple exemplars help these students generalize the new vocabulary concepts to a variety of situations. Multiple exemplars also expand students' *mental maps* of meanings of new words. The Creative Collages strategy involves students in a hands-on activity that helps them learn the words faster and retain the words longer. Creative Collages is a fun, low-anxiety activity in which students are not forced to produce orally unless they are comfortable doing so.

Ideas for Use

➤ The clinician can photocopy pictures from each unit. The students may color these pictures and use them on the collage.

➤ The collage can be focused on only one unit, or it can integrate and combine vocabulary from a number of units.

➤ The clinician can bring magazines, and the students can cut out pictures that are related to the theme of the collage. For example, if there is a food collage (Unit 3), students can cut out pictures of food from magazines and paste these pictures onto the collage.

➤ The clinician (or students who write) can write labels for each picture so that the pictures on the collage can be paired with written words.

➤ The collage can be used for many types of games. For example, students can select a picture and the other students can guess what it is. The other students might ask questions such as, "Is it a fruit?" or "Is it something cold?"

➤ The collage can be used for phonological awareness activities. For example, the clinician might say, "I'm looking at a picture that rhymes with *berries*." (The word is *cherries*.)

Treatment Strategy 8: Using Questions to Assess Comprehension in Instructional Activities

Background & Rationale   ELL students with LLD need to learn to answer comprehension questions appropriately. However, cultural differences among students may predispose some of them to not answering questions in the way expected by mainstream culture. The following examples can be used to ask students questions in a manner that is most likely to elicit good answers. Examples of inappropriate ways to ask questions are also shown.

Example

To successfully assess students' comprehension:

➤ *Ask for a brief summary of what was just said. For example:*
   - Heidi, what have we been talking about?
   - Elisa, you be the teacher and tell us the story we just read in your own words.

➤ *Ask students to speculate about and expand on the information that was just presented. For example:*
   - Mario, can you think of another example of...?
   - Estera, how would you have done things differently than...?
   - Who would like to tell us what they think will happen in the end?

➤ *Ask students to express opinions about the material. For example:*
   - Sergei, what do you think of that?
   - Manuela, what didn't you like about this story?
   - Samuel, what was your favorite thing about the lesson we just did?

➤ *Use clarification requests. For example:*
   - Bill, when you said that the apple was good, did you mean that...?
   - Jaime, can you tell me what you mean when you say that...?

Types of questions to avoid:

➤ *Run-on, multiple questions. For example:*
   - "What happened at the end of the story? Why did the girl go back home? What would have happened if she hadn't gone back home?" English learners may be confused by hearing more than one question at a time.

➤ *Rhetorical questions.* Some students who are still learning English may have difficulty distinguishing between rhetorical questions and those that require a response.

➤ *Questions that clash with students' cultural styles. For example:*
   - "Is that clear? Did you understand that? Are there any questions?" Students from some cultural groups have been taught that it is a sign of disrespect to indicate to the authority figure that information presented has not been understood.

Sources: Brice & Roseberry-McKibbin, 1999; Roseberry-McKibbin, 1995

ELL students with LLD need to build listening skills as they learn vocabulary. The Lively Listening strategy uses the principle of reauditorization to help these students rehearse what they hear silently in their minds. This strategy is very helpful for promoting success in the classroom.

Example (Unit 4: Self-Care Items)

Clinician: We are going to work on listening and learning to remember the words we hear. Let's try this out loud first. I am going to say two words, and you repeat them after me. *Comb, soap.* Say *comb, soap.*

Students: Comb, soap.

Clinican: Good job! Let's try another one. *Shoes, socks, pants.* Say *shoes, socks, pants.*

Students: Shoes, socks, pants.

Clinician: Great! Now, let's try saying these next words quietly in our heads. Listen carefully and say these words to yourself quietly in your heads. *Hat, tie.* (pause) Now, what did I just say?

Students: Hat, tie.

Clinician: Nice work! You said those words quietly to yourself in your heads. That helped you to remember them. Let's make this a little more challenging. I need to get dressed. I need to put on my *shirt, pants,* and *shoes.* Say those things to yourself quietly in your heads. *Shirt, pants, shoes.* (pause) What did I just say?

Students: Shirt, pants, shoes.

Clinician: Wow! You got it. Juan, it's your turn. You tell us two things you want to wear, and we will repeat those things quietly in our heads. Then you call on someone to tell you what you said.

Juan: I need to wear my *boots* and *coat.*

Clinician: Juan, call on someone to tell you what you just said.

Juan: Rosa, what am I going to wear?

Rosa: Boots and coat.

Treatment Strategy 10: Copycat Circle

After the clinician has taught students how to reauditorize information they hear, Copycat Circle can be introduced. Literature in both speech pathology and second-language acquisition stresses the benefits of repetition for learning of new concepts. When words are used in meaningful messages, repetition facilitates the retention of information. Thus, when students repeat, they must repeat things that have meaning for them. Copycat Circle helps students use new vocabulary words in phrases and sentences, and should be used for vocabulary words that students have already become familiar with. Students can imitate each other and the clinician. Clinicians can create many varieties of this activity.

Note: If the students' English proficiency is not high enough, the clinician can provide all of the models. However, if students have enough English proficiency, they can give examples for the rest of the group to repeat.

Example 1 (Unit 7: Safety and Survival)

Clinician: Now we're going to play a game called Copycat Circle. We will use our new safety words that we have been learning. Say these things right after me three times, just the way I do. For example, let's try: *Poison! Stop! Danger!*

Students: Poison! Stop! Danger!
Poison! Stop! Danger!
Poison! Stop! Danger!

Clinician: Great! Poison means something that could hurt or kill us if we touch or eat it. So we need to stop, because there is danger when we touch or eat poison. Let's try another one. *Emergency!* Call the *police!*

Students: Emergency! Call the police!
Emergency! Call the police!
Emergency! Call the police!

Clinician: Nice copying. What does *emergency* mean?

Students: (Explain the meaning of *emergency*.)

Clinician: Yes, and that is why we call the police.

Example 2 (Unit 5: Animals)

Clinician: Let's play a game called Copycat Circle. I am going to a farm and then to a zoo. When I tell you what animals I am going to see, say these animals after me three times. I am going to a farm, and I will see a *chicken, pig,* and *cow.*

Students: Chicken, pig, cow.
Chicken, pig, cow.

Chicken, pig, cow.

Clinician: Yes! I will see a chicken, pig, and cow. Graciela, let's pretend you are going to the zoo. What are four animals you will see at the zoo? Tell us, and we will say those animals three times.

Graciela: *Zebra, lion, tiger, monkey.*

All: Zebra, lion, tiger, monkey.
Zebra, lion, tiger, monkey.
Zebra, lion, tiger, monkey.

Example 3 (Unit 6: Time, Weather, and Seasons)

Clinician: We're going to play a game called Copycat Circle. Someone will use time/weather/season vocabulary words in a sentence, and you repeat what they say three times. I will start. This *week* will be *windy* and *cold*.

Students: This week will be windy and cold.
This week will be windy and cold.
This week will be windy and cold.

Clinician: Nice listening. I am going to pick someone else now. Hassim, why don't you give us a weather sentence and we will repeat it three times?

Hassim: It's *hot* when the *sun* shines.

All: It's hot when the sun shines
It's hot when the sun shines.
It's hot when the sun shines.

Clinician: Thank you, Hassim. Phun, why don't you give us a sentence using the word *calendar* and we'll repeat it three times?

Phun: A *calendar* has *weeks* and *months*.

All: A calendar has weeks and months.
A calendar has weeks and months.
A calendar has weeks and months.

25

Treatment Strategy 11: Direction Detective

ELL students with LLD need to take the vocabulary they learn and follow directions using the vocabulary. Following directions is an extremely important classroom skill. The clinician can use the picture cards in the vocabulary units and have students follow directions using the cards. This is especially good for students in the early stages of English language learning if these students are reluctant to speak out loud in English. (**Note**: The whole group listens to the directions, and then the clinician names the student to carry out the directions.)

Example 1 (Unit 1: School Items)

Clinician: Let's take some of our pictures and follow directions. We'll use our school cards. Here are pictures of a *table, chair, pencil*, and *book*. Listen, and I will call on someone to be my first Direction Detective. Dorinna, put the *chair* under the *table*.

Dorinna: (Puts the chair under the table.)

Clinician: Good job! The chair is under the table. Let's do another one. Put the *pencil* and *book* next to the *table*. Josefa, please?

Josefa: (Puts the pencil and book next to the table.)

Example 2 (Unit 3: Food Items)

Clinician: I am going shopping and I need you to help me remember what to buy. Here is my shopping cart. Listen, and I will call on you to be my Direction Detective. Please put *cheese, butter*, and *corn* into my cart. Wong, will you do that?

Wong: (Puts the pictures of the items in the shopping cart.)

Clinician: Thank you, Wong! Now, why don't you say three more foods that need to go into the cart, and tell someone to put them in there?

Wong: I need *carrots, potatoes*, and *grapes*. Ralph, please put them into the cart.

Ralph: (Puts them into the cart.)

Background & Rationale Many ELL learners, especially those with LLD, do not know how to initiate and continue conversations with native English speakers. By using patterns in group activities, clinicians can teach vocabulary while they are also teaching simple interactive language patterns. Additionally, students learn basic morphosyntactic skills in English in a nonthreatening way where errors are not overtly corrected. Students do not feel threatened because (1) everyone is involved in the activity, (2) the patterns are easy to follow, and (3) the patterns are presented in a playful way. Additional learning is facilitated because the patterns are tied to a theme.

Example 1 (Unit 1: School Items)

(Give each student a picture card from Unit 1.)

Clinician: (Shows a picture of the *desk*.) What do I have? I have a *desk*. (To student A.) What do you have?

Student A: I have a *pencil*. (To student B.) What do you have?

Student B: I have a *ruler*. (To student C.) What do you have?

(Students then continue around the group.)

Example 2 (Unit 4: Self-Care Items)

(Give each student a picture card from Unit 4.)

Clinician: (Holds up picture of *socks*.) What am I wearing? I'm wearing *socks*. (To student A.) What are you wearing?

Student A: I'm wearing *shoes*. (To student B.) What are you wearing?

Student B: I'm wearing *glasses*. (To student C.) What are you wearing?

Student C: I'm wearing *boots*. (To student D.) What are you wearing?

(Students then continue around the group.)

Treatment Strategy 13: **Rhyming Reels**

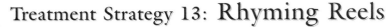

Background & Rationale ELL students with LLD need lots of repetition to learn new words. They also need to practice early-developing English structures such as *-ing*; plural (*-s*); the words *these* and *this*; articles *the, a, an*; and forms of "to be" (*are* and *is*). This simple game provides repetition with vocabulary words as well as lots of practice with early-developing English structures. The game can be played in a "chant" to add some variety.

Clinician: Let's play a game called Rhyming Reels. I will choose a few pictures and show you how to do this. Then you can take a picture out of the bag and say a rhyme of the picture just like I did.

Example 1 (Unit 2: Body Parts)

Clinician: (Selects a picture of hands.) I see *hands*. What do I see? These are hands looking right at me! (Selects a picture of feet.) I see *feet*. What do I see? These are feet looking right at me! (Selects a picture of a mouth.) I see a *mouth*. What do I see? This is a mouth looking right at me! Okay, let's let someone else take a turn. Alexandr, how about you?

Alexandr: (Selects a picture of a stomach.) I see a *stomach*. What do I see? This is a stomach looking right at me!

Clinician: Nice going. Evita, draw a card and let's have the whole group do it together.

Evita: (Selects a picture of a nose.)

All: I see a *nose*. What do I see? This is a nose looking right at me!

Example 2 (Unit 5: Animals)

Clinician: (Explains game as above.) We are going to lay all of our animal cards on the table. When I give you an animal card, you match it to the one just like it and say the rhyme that goes with it. For example, here is a picture of a *lion*. I will get the other picture of the lion and say, "I see a *lion*. What do I see? Now I see two lions looking at me!" Tonya, here is a picture of a *bear*. Will you match the bear to the other bear picture and say the rhyme?

Tonya: I see a *bear*. What do I see? I see two bears looking at me!

Students who are learning English and have an accompanying LLD frequently benefit from rhythm and music. Rhythm and music help students learn vocabulary more quickly and remember it longer because the right hemisphere of the brain is utilized. Clapping also allows for multisensory learning. In addition, rhyming facilitates phonological awareness skills.

Example (Unit 2: Body Parts)

Clinician: We are going to do some silly rhymes with our body parts words. I will do a few for you, and then I want you to try to guess what rhymes with the word.

(**Note**: Chant these rhythmically or sing them to the melody of "Row Row Row Your Boat"; students may also clap each word.)

Widdley waddly woddley pace; I'm thinking of a *face.*
Widdley waddly woddley breeze; I'm thinking of some *knees.*
Widdley waddly woddley doze; I'm thinking of a *nose.*
Widdley waddly woddley sack; I'm thinking of a *back.*

Now, I am going to leave the word out and see if you can guess it.

Widdley waddly woddley fair; I'm thinking of some _____. (*hair*)
Widdley waddly woddley bands; I'm thinking of some _____. (*hands*)

(**Note**: You can ask if any students would like to try singing and having the others guess what word should be placed in the blank.)

Treatment Strategy 15: Descriptive Drawings

When ELL students with LLD learn vocabulary in a second language, they frequently learn to give one-word labels to pictures of objects. However, they have difficulty with formal descriptions of these objects. It is very important for ELL students with LLD to describe things accurately so that listeners know what is being discussed. The Descriptive Drawing strategy is a fun, sometimes hilarious way to help students achieve description skills. Use this strategy after students are familiar enough with the vocabulary in a unit to describe the words so that others can draw them.

Example (Unit 4: Self-Care Items)

Clinician: We are going to play a fun game today. I will show one of you a picture that no one else gets to see. The person who sees the picture will describe it, and everyone else will draw what they hear. So, the person who talks about the picture will need to tell all the details so that everyone else can draw a good picture! Tamiko, why don't you start?

Tamiko: (Picks a picture of a *toothbrush*.) It's made of plastic. It's skinny and has bristles at the end. (Student goes on to describe the toothbrush.)

The clinician needs to help the student with the description if the student does not have the vocabulary to describe the picture well. Thus, the clinician might ask questions such as "Tamiko, tell the others how long it is. Is it two inches long? Seven inches long? What do you think?"

At the end of this activity, the students show their pictures and compare them to the one held by the student who gave the description.

As a variation, the clinician can write on a board everything that has been said already. These characteristics that have already been described can serve as a reminder to students who have challenges with auditory memory.

If key elements were omitted, the clinician can write down these elements and thus give the student specific feedback about how the explanation could have been more thorough. This specific feedback will help students understand where they may be experiencing communication breakdowns with their listeners.

Background & Rationale Students who are LLD and learning English as another language need to develop their literacy skills. A major challenge for many of these students, however, is that they are nonliterate in their first languages. Their language-learning disabilities make it difficult to learn to read in English, and thus these students frequently do little or no reading. Also, there may be little or no reading in the students' homes. A solution to this situation is wordless books. Students can create these and "read" them to their peers, teachers, siblings, parents, or caregivers. The "reading" of wordless books promotes English language development, literacy, and enhances overall academic success.

Ideas for Use

➤ Students can color the vocabulary cards in each unit. They can then make books with the cards, gluing the cards onto each page.

➤ The pages can be left with just pictures and no captions. Students can tell the story orally.

➤ If students can write, they may write captions for each page.

➤ If students do not write, they can dictate their stories to the clinician, who can write the captions on each page.

➤ Students can share their stories orally in small groups (e.g., speech-language therapy groups).

➤ Students can share their stories in front of their classes.

➤ The books can be laminated and sent home so that the students can tell the stories to their families.

➤ Students can make a wordless book for each vocabulary unit. They can also make wordless books that integrate the vocabulary words from various units. For example, students might make a wordless book using cards from the Food Items and Animals units. Or, they might make a wordless book using cards from the School Items, Safety and Survival, and Body Parts units.

Treatment Strategy 17: Choral Reading

Background & Rationale Many beginning ELL students with LLD are very reluctant to speak in their second language of English. However, if they do not have to speak alone, they may be more willing to verbalize. Choral reading is an enjoyable, low-anxiety, language activity. Choral reading helps students learn the intonation of English stories and poems. It expands their vocabularies and improves their reading fluency.

Ideas for Use

➤ In choral reading, the clinician selects a poem or story related to the vocabulary unit being taught. For example, for Unit 6, the clinician might select a story relating to weather and seasons. The clinician reads the poem or story to the students several times while showing the students the words. Students may even be given their own copy of the story or poem.

➤ After hearing the clinician read the material six or seven times, the students can join in as best they can. They may even act out the story or poem.

➤ As a variation, the clinician may allow the students to fill in words after they have heard the material a number of times.

➤ Another variation is as follows: After the students have done choral readings of four or five stories or poems, the clinician can write down the title of each story or poem on 3" x 5" index cards. A group of students can draw a card and pantomime or act out the story or poem. The student or students who first guess the title can receive points. Whoever has the most points at the end of the game wins!

Background & Rationale For ELL students with LLD, reading in a second language is a major challenge. This is especially true for those students who do not have a literacy base in their first language. While these students need decoding skills, they also need to develop sight vocabulary for common words in English. The 20 words below are some of the most common words in English print. If students learn to sightread these words, their reading fluency will be greatly assisted.

Ideas for Use

Clinicians can reproduce the chart below and post it on a wall, reviewing the words often. It is best to begin by reading the words aloud, having the students listen first. The words can then be taught in groups of five. Students can engage in choral reading to review the words. Students can also receive individual copies of the reproduced chart and take it home to review. The words may also be paired with vocabulary words from Units 1-7. For example, the clinician might write phrases, such as the following from Unit 7 (Safety and Survival), on paper or on the board: (These phrases can be reviewed and read aloud individually or in chorus.)

- **the** ambulance
- **you** stop
- **the** restrooms **are** private
- **they are** closed

Wonderful Words

the	of	and	a
to	in	you	is
that	it	at	he
for	on	are	as
with	his	they	be

Adapted from Mason & Au, 1990; Peregoy & Boyle, 1997

Treatment Strategy 19: Wall Words

As has been emphasized, the repetition needed by ELL students with LLD is very great. The strategy of Wall Words gives students visual and verbal repetition of the new vocabulary words they learn. This strategy also enhances phonological awareness and sound-symbol association, skill areas that are fundamental to success in literacy. In addition, students are assisted in remembering the spelling of each new word they have learned.

Ideas for Use

➤ Post a large piece of butcher paper on a wall. Write your students' names under the appropriate letters. As the students learn new vocabulary words from each unit, they can write these words under the appropriate letter of the alphabet. (The illustration below displays a partial Wall Word chart). For nonwriters, you can write the words for the students. Review the wall words each day.

➤ As a variation on this, you can enhance students' phonological awareness skills through silly sounds or rhyming. For example, say, "I am going to give you a silly, made-up word. It rhymes with one of the words on the wall chart. The word is *chog*. Who can find the real word that rhymes with *chog*?"

Aa	**Bb**	**Cc**	**Dd**
Arisbel	Bettina	Caleb	Dandansoy
animal	Bobby	comb	dress
apple	brush	cow	duck
ambulance	boots	cat	dog
arms	belt	corn	desk
	bus	carrot	day
	book	calendar	

Background & Rationale Listening comprehension and word retrieval are two areas that are frequently very difficult for ELL students with LLD. In addition, describing things clearly is challenging in a second language when a language-learning disability is present. Playing the game "I Spy" gives these students opportunities to listen and retrieve exact vocabulary words to match the clinician's descriptions. It also helps these students increase their verbal skills through encouraging them to describe things clearly enough for listeners to guess their meaning.

Ideas for Use

➤ Play the "I Spy" guessing game using the wall words. For example, you might say, "I spy a word on the wall chart. It is an animal that usually lives on a farm and gives us milk. This animal says 'moo.' What word am I thinking of?"

➤ You might also lay out pictures of vocabulary words and describe one of the pictures. For example, you might say, "I spy something we eat that is yellow. It is a vegetable. What am I thinking of?" The student who guesses which word is being described (*corn*) gets to keep the card. The student with the most cards at the end of the game wins.

➤ As a variation on this strategy, have a student choose a wall word and give the description. If the student has difficulty with the description, encourage her to tell the group what letter the word starts with.

➤ Students can also play the game using vocabulary picture cards from a bag or surprise box.

Treatment Strategy 21: **Supersleuth Co-op**

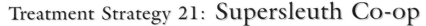

Background & Rationale ELL students with LLD need to learn formal definitions of words and how to find those words in the dictionary. But sometimes this can take a long time. Many experts recommend cooperative learning to accomplish difficult or lengthy tasks. In cooperative learning, students work together on a project. This is an excellent way to not only facilitate learning of information but also to promote social interaction skills. This activity facilitates cooperative learning, conceptualization of formal definitions of vocabulary words, and the ability to look up words in a dictionary.

Example (Unit 6: Time, Weather, and Seasons)

Clinician: We are going to use our dictionaries to look up some words about time and weather. Each one of you in the group (assuming there are five students in the group) needs to find four words and write their definitions. You can draw pictures if you like. Then we will share our definitions and pictures with everyone else and make our own time/weather/seasons dictionary.

Give each student four words and, if needed, assist the students in looking up words in the dictionary and writing the definitions. Students may also help each other look up words. Encourage students to draw pictures to accompany their definitions. Have students create a personal dictionary by putting their definitions with pictures in a 3-ring binder. This fun cooperative learning activity helps students learn vocabulary as well as working together toward a final product.

Other Activities

Here are some additional ways students can use their new words and definitions:

➤ Try to write several different sentences using a word.

➤ Write a paragraph or story that uses all the words that they have defined.

➤ Write a sentence, leaving a blank space for one of the words. See if the other students can guess which word is needed to complete the sentence.

➤ Create a crossword puzzle using their words.

Background & Rationale As students learn dictionary and vocabulary skills, it is helpful (for writers) to write about the words they are looking up. Writing increases retention of information as well as promoting literacy skills.

Ideas for Use

As students complete the Supersleuth Co-op activity, they can write about their words using the next page, which can be reproduced as often as necessary.

Name _____

Date _____

My word is _____.

I found my word on page _____.

My word means:

_____

_____

_____

_____

_____

Here's a sentence using my word:

_____

_____

_____

_____

Here's another sentence using my word:

_____

_____

_____

_____

> **Background & Rationale**   ELL students with LLD need to develop their abilities to predict, to derive meaning from a context, and to focus on a whole passage rather than on isolated segments. *Cloze* is the elimination of key words in a context. Cloze activities help ESL students read in segments rather than word by word. These activities can be done orally for nonreaders but are best done in written form for students who read and write.

Example 1 (Unit 6: Time, Weather, and Seasons)

It was a beautiful day, and the _____ was shining brightly in the sky. There were no clouds, so it didn't look like _____. Mario smelled the beautiful _____, and was happy that the weather was _____. In Mexico, sometimes there was rain and loud _____ during storms. Also, there could be flashes of _____ in the sky.

Example 2 (Unit 7: Safety and Survival)

Gretha heard a siren. She wondered if it was a(n) _____ driving quickly down the street. She knew something bad must have suddenly happened—it must be an _____. She hoped it wasn't a _____ where something was burning down. Maybe someone had eaten some _____ and suddenly felt very sick. She hoped that the _____ who had gotten to the place first in his police car would be able to _____ the people who might be hurt. Gretha was glad someone had used the _____ to dial 911.

Treatment Strategy 24: Mystery Word

Background & Rationale The intrinsic reading difficulties of ELL students with LLD make it imperative that they develop basic visual closure and sound symbol association skills. In Mystery Word, vocabulary words are reviewed and students have fun developing these skills. This activity also helps promote overall phonological awareness in students.

Example 1 (Unit 6: Time, Weather, and Seasons)

Clinician: I am going to write spaces for the word I am thinking of. You will need to guess letters like they do on the show "Wheel of Fortune." (Explain how the game is played, if necessary.) Whoever guesses the word gets a point, and whoever gets the most points wins. Look at these blanks here.

_____ _____ _____ _____

How many blanks are there? Yes, four. This weather word has four letters in it. Who would like to guess the first letter? (**Note**: The word is *cold.*)

Rebekah: I guess an "h."

Clinician: Nice try. Let's write down "h" in our column of letters that are not in this weather word. How about someone else?

Rosario: I guess "l."

Clinician: Yes—right! (writes in "l")

(The game continues until the word is solved.)

Mystery Word	
Letters guessed that aren't in the Mystery Word h g s x r	___ ___ L ___

Treatment Strategy 25: Interactive Dialogue Journals

Background & Rationale

ELL students with LLD need lots of practice in written language. Writing helps students with learning and retention of new vocabulary, and it assists in development of overall literacy skills. Ideally, writing practice would occur in a nonthreatening, safe context that was supported by an empathetic adult who would respond primarily to the content of the writing. Interactive dialogue journals meet these criteria. Students make entries, and the clinician responds in writing with a question or statement that continues the conversation. This enables ELL students with LLD to engage in a functional, written communication activity and to improve writing skills.

Example (Unit 7: Safety and Survival)

Clinician: I would like each of you to write something about safety. It can be anything you would like. When you are done, I will write back to you. When you read what I have written, you can write back to me.

Student: I try to be safe by not playing with matches. My dad told me that could start a fire.

Clinician: I'm really glad you stay safe by not playing with matches. Your dad is right! Did your dad tell you anything else about safety?

Student: Yeah—my dad, he says to not talk to strangers because I can get in trouble.

Clinician: He's right about that, too. What can you do if a stranger approaches you and tries to touch or grab you?

Student: Um, I don't know.

Clinician: There are some important rules about talking to strangers. We'll discuss them on Wednesday.

Source: Peregoy & Boyle, 1997

Part 2

Introduction

How to Use Units 1-7

➤ Each unit begins with an **Annual Goal** of increasing overall receptive and expressive vocabulary skills. Hierarchically sequenced, measurable IEP objectives/benchmarks are provided for teaching new vocabulary to students.

➤ The beginning of each unit also contains an **Annual Goal** of increasing phonological awareness skills. Hierarchically sequenced, measurable objectives are provided for teaching these skills.

➤ In each unit, there are reproducible sheets for documenting pretest and posttest results of skills measured by each objective.

➤ Each unit has **Vocabulary Pictures** depicting every new vocabulary word. These pictures can be reproduced and used in a number of ways. Students can color the pictures, the pictures can be duplicated and made into a "Concentration" game, or you can send copies of the cards home for use as flash cards. The possibilities are limitless!

➤ In each unit, there are also reproducible **Word Cards** with the printed words on them. These cards can be used for a variety of different teaching activities.

➤ Each unit contains **Vocabulary Word Definitions** of the words being taught. The definitions have deliberately been kept simple and concrete so that ELL students with LLD will have little difficulty learning them.

➤ There are no specific reproducible activities for each objective. For example, in Objective 1 of each unit, the student is asked to point to pictures. Thus, for Objective 1, the SLP can do this easily with no reproducible materials to enhance therapy. However, for objectives requiring more time and thought, there are reproducible materials in each unit. For example, Objective 7 asks the student to use a target word in a sentence. There are reproducible activities to enhance the facilitation of this objective.

➤ Each unit is designed to be used flexibly with students who are nonliterate as well as those who do some basic English reading,

43

writing, and spelling. Use your judgment, according to each individual student's ability, as to which objectives and materials are appropriate for each student.

➤ As students progress through each unit, you may incorporate vocabulary items from previous units. This will facilitate integration of the material being learned and add redundance for each concept being taught.

➤ In each unit, Brown's (1973) earliest-developing morphemes are incorporated into activities. Although these morphemes, such as *-ing*, plural *-s*, possessive *-s* , and regular past tense *-ed*, are not explicitly targeted or taught, they are modeled frequently to provide exposure for students. Frequent exposure enhances learning.

Additional Therapy Tips

Most of the premises underlying this section are described in the introduction to the book. However, the following are additional ideas and therapy tips:

➤ Remember that students who are learning a second language need, in the early stages, to focus on comprehension. These students may be silent for some period as they attempt to understand the second language. Do not force students to produce verbally in English before they are ready.

➤ Remember that reading aloud to students (incorporating vocabulary from the units) builds language and literacy competence. Reading aloud to students stimulates an interest in reading as well as aiding in the acquisition of the vocabulary and grammar of printed English (Krashen, 1996; Trelease, 1995).

➤ Focus on communication of meaning. Do not overtly correct students' grammatical errors in English, but rather model correct grammatical patterns.

➤ Encourage students, when they are ready, to interact frequently with one another (Goldstein, 2000). This will give them additional practice with the vocabulary they are learning.

➤ Remember that phonological awareness is foundational to reading, writing, and spelling in English. Development of basic phonological awareness skills will promote mastery of English literacy skills (Goldsworthy, 1998; Goldsworthy, 2001; Robertson & Salter, 1997).

➤ Imitation of the clinician and repetition of new structures and concepts is one of the very best ways to help ELL LLD students truly learn and retain this new information.

➤ Students learn best when a multi-modal approach incorporating seeing, listening, speaking, and kinesthetic activities is used. Music also helps because it utilizes the right hemisphere of the brain.

➤ Students will learn new words faster when the words are accompanied by sensory-motor activities (Ventriglia, 1982). Thus, for example, students may act out words or draw pictures of words they are learning. Again, these kinesthetic or sensory-motor activities will promote much faster learning than if students just hear the new words.

➤ It is best to have multiple exemplars of each vocabulary item. Ideally, for example, when learning about a *dress* in the Self-Care Items Unit, the clinician can show many pictures of different kinds of dresses. Or, in the Animals Unit, the clinician can show pictures of different kinds of *dogs* and even bring in several toy dogs for students to see and manipulate.

➤ Create your own games and activities to supplement activities in each unit.

➤ And, finally—Repeat, Repeat, Repeat, and have fun!

45

Vocabulary Objectives

Annual Goal

Student will demonstrate increased receptive and expressive vocabulary skills.

Short-Term Objectives/Benchmarks

Objective 1

When the clinician verbally gives school item target vocabulary words, the student will point to pictures of these items with 80% accuracy.

Clinician: Marisol, point to *desk*. Point to *chair*.
Student: (Points to each named picture.)

Objective 2

When the clinician holds up a picture and says, "Is this a(n) _____?" the student will verbally or nonverbally indicate *yes* or *no* with 80% accuracy.

Clinician: (Holds up a picture of *ruler*.) Carl, is this a pencil?
Student: No. (Says verbally or shakes head *no.*)

Clinician: (Holds up a picture of *scissors*.) Juanita, are these scissors?
Student: Yes. (Says verbally or shakes head *yes.*)

Objective 3

When the clinician gives a 1-2 sentence verbal description of a target word/concept and gives the student two choices of answers, the student will verbally supply the correct answer with 80% accuracy.

Clinician: Listen, Truong. This is usually made of wood and has an eraser. Students use this to write with. Is it a *pencil* or *crayons*?
Student: Pencil.

Objective 4

When shown pictures of school item target vocabulary words, the student will give verbal, one-word labels with 80% accuracy.

Clinician: (Shows picture of a book.) Anna, what's this?
Student: Book.

Objective 5

When asked to verbally list 3-5 items in a given category, the student will do so with 80% accuracy.

Clinician: Liza, tell me the names of four different things we find in a classroom at school.

Student: Desk, chair, crayons, scissors.

Objective 6

When asked to define a target vocabulary word, the student will give a 5+ word verbal description with 80% accuracy.

Clinician: Roberto, what is a *playground*?

Student: It is a large place outside where students play.

Objective 7

When given a school item target vocabulary word, the student will use the word in a sentence with 80% accuracy.

Clinician: Carlos, please use the word *paper* in a sentence.

Student: We write on paper.

For more advanced students: (written language)

Objective 8

When presented with a paragraph or word list containing the school item target vocabulary word, the student will find and read the word out loud with 80% accuracy.

Clinician: Manuela, look at this story. Please find the word *desk*, and read the word to me after you find it.

Student: (Reads story.) Desk. (Reads word aloud.)

Objective 9

When asked to spell a target vocabulary word, the student will spell the word out loud with 80% accuracy.

Clinician: Jaime, please spell the word *teacher*.

Student: (Spells the word out loud.)

Objective 10

When given a target vocabulary word, the student will write a sentence containing the word with 80% accuracy.

Clinician: Estera, please write the word *bus* in a sentence.

Student: (Writes a sentence containing the word *bus*.)

The Source for Bilingual Students with Language Disorders

48

Phonological Awareness Objectives

Annual Goal

Student will demonstrate increased phonological awareness skills.

Short-Term Objectives/Benchmarks

Objective 11

With 80% accuracy, the student will count the number of words in a sentence that is prewritten or that the student has written.

Clinician:	Look, Paige. Here is a sentence in our story. Count how many words are in that sentence.
Student:	(Counts the number of words in the sentence.)

Clinician:	Xuehue, you wrote a good sentence using the word *pencil.* Please count how many words are in your sentence.
Student:	(Counts the number of words in the sentence.)

Objective 12

When given a target vocabulary word, the student will identify the number of syllables in that word with 80% accuracy.

Clinician:	Roman, how many syllables are in the word *scissors*?
Student:	Two.

Objective 13

When given a target vocabulary word, the student will identify the number of sounds in that word with 80% accuracy.

Clinician:	Mariel, how many sounds are in the word *desk*?
Student:	Four.

Objective 14

When the student hears a word that rhymes with a target vocabulary word, the student will identify that word verbally or nonverbally with 80% accuracy.

Clinician:	Tatiana, color the picture that rhymes with *hair*.
Student:	(Colors the picture of the chair.)

Clinician:	Favio, what school word rhymes with *fuss*?
Student:	Bus.

Objective **15**
When the student hears the speech pathologist say a target vocabulary word phoneme by phoneme, that student will demonstrate sound blending skills by stating the whole word with 80% accuracy.

Clinician: Antonia, what word is this? /P/-/a/-/p/-/er/.
Student: Paper.

Objective **16**
When given a target vocabulary word, the student will identify the first sound in that word upon request with 80% accuracy.

Clinician: Listen, Vladimir. *Pencil.* What's the first sound in that word?
Student: /p/

Objective **17**
When given a target vocabulary word, the student will identify the last sound in that word upon request with 80% accuracy.

Clinician: Listen, Leilani. *Teacher.* What's the last sound in that word?
Student: /r/

50

Target Words Unit 1: School Items	Objective 1 point to pictures		Objective 2 yes/no		Objective 3 2-choice answer		Objective 4 1-word label		Objective 5 list items		Objective 6 verbal definition	
+ Correct − Incorrect	Pretest Date	Posttest Date	Pretest Date	Posttest Date	Pretest Date	Posttest Date	Pretest Date	Posttest Date	Pretest Date	Posttest Date	Pretest Date	Posttest Date
1. bathroom												
2. book												
3. bus												
4. calendar												
5. chair												
6. classroom												
7. computer												
8. crayons												
9. desk												
10. library												
11. map												
12. notebook												
13. paper												
14. pencil												
15. playground												
16. ruler												
17. scissors												
18. student												
19. table												
20. teacher												
% Correct	% Correct		% Correct		% Correct		% Correct		% Correct		% Correct	

Unit 1: School Items

Target Words / Unit 1: School Items (+ Correct − Incorrect)	Objective 7 — say word in sentence (Pretest Date)	(Posttest Date)	Objective 8 — read word in paragraph (Pretest Date)	(Posttest Date)	Objective 9 — spell the word (Pretest Date)	(Posttest Date)	Objective 10 — write word in sentence (Pretest Date)	(Posttest Date)	Objective 11 — count words in sentence (Pretest Date)	(Posttest Date)	Objective 12 — count syllables in word (Pretest Date)	(Posttest Date)
1. bathroom												
2. book												
3. bus												
4. calendar												
5. chair												
6. classroom												
7. computer												
8. crayons												
9. desk												
10. library												
11. map												
12. notebook												
13. paper												
14. pencil												
15. playground												
16. ruler												
17. scissors												
18. student												
19. table												
20. teacher												
% Correct	% Correct	% Correct	% Correct	% Correct	% Correct	% Correct	% Correct	% Correct	% Correct	% Correct	% Correct	% Correct

The Source for Bilingual Students with Language Disorders

Unit 1: School Items

Target Words	Objective 13		Objective 14		Objective 15		Objective 16		Objective 17	
Unit 1: School Items	identify number of sounds in word		identify rhyming word		sound blending		identify first sound in word		identify last sound in word	
+ Correct − Incorrect	Pretest Date	Posttest Date	Pretest Date	Posttest Date	Pretest Date	Posttest Date	Pretest Date	Posttest Date	Pretest Date	Posttest Date
1. bathroom										
2. book										
3. bus										
4. calendar										
5. chair										
6. classroom										
7. computer										
8. crayons										
9. desk										
10. library										
11. map										
12. notebook										
13. paper										
14. pencil										
15. playground										
16. ruler										
17. scissors										
18. student										
19. table										
20. teacher										
	% Correct	% Correct	% Correct	% Correct	% Correct	% Correct	% Correct	% Correct	% Correct	% Correct

Vocabulary Pictures: Cut these pictures apart to use in the activities that follow.

Vocabulary Pictures: Cut these pictures apart to use in the activities that follow.

There are many uses for these Word Cards, including having your students pair them with the picture cards, reading the words aloud (if students are able), or copying the words on the lines for practice. Use these vocabulary words in any way you see fit.

bathroom	book	bus
calendar	chair	classroom
computer	crayons	desk
library	map	notebook
paper	pencil	playground
ruler	scissors	student
table	teacher	

Vocabulary Word Definitions

bathroom A place where people go when they need to use the toilet. There are toilets, sinks, and sometimes mirrors.

book Something people read. It has pages and words. Sometimes it has pictures.

bus A large vehicle that picks children up and brings them to school. It also takes children home at the end of the day.

calendar Tells us the day, date, month, and year. It is usually on the wall.

chair People sit in this piece of furniture. It usually has a back and four legs.

classroom A room where teachers teach students. Students usually sit in chairs at desks or tables in this room.

computer A piece of electronic equipment. People can type on the keyboard and use it for drawing, writing, playing games, and lots of other things.

crayons Come in many different colors. We draw, color, and write with them.

desk What a student sits at. It has a flat top for writing, drawing, and reading.

library A place where we read and check out books.

map Shows a drawing of a place or places. It usually shows cities, countries, mountains, rivers, and oceans.

notebook A book where notes are kept. It can have three rings or be spiral-bound.

paper Something we write on. We can also cut it and make things with it. It is often white but can be other colors too.

pencil Usually made of wood and has an eraser. It needs to be sharpened. Students write with it.

playground A large place outside where students play. Recess usually happens here.

ruler An instrument used to measure things and draw lines. It is straight and is one foot long. It has 12 inches marked on it.

scissors A tool used to cut paper and other things. They are usually made of metal and they are sharp.

student A person in the class who studies and learns.

table A piece of furniture that people sit around. It is flat and you can do a lot of things on it like read, write, color, and make things.

teacher A man or woman who teaches the class.

Activity 1: School Items

Have your students complete each definition with a word from the box. (Do this orally with nonreading students.)

desk	ruler	calendar	crayons	table
pencil	paper	scissors	book	notebook

1. A _____ is usually made of wood and has an eraser. It needs to be sharpened. Students write with it.

2. A _____ is a piece of furniture that people sit around. It is flat and you can do a lot of things on it like read, write, color, and make things.

3. We write on _____. We can also cut it and make things with it. It is often white but can be other colors too.

4. We use _____ to cut paper and other things. They are usually made of metal and they are sharp.

5. A student sits at a_____. It has a flat top for writing, drawing, and reading.

6. A _____ is something people read. It has pages and words. Sometimes it has pictures.

7. A _____ is a book where notes are kept. It can have three rings or be spiral-bound.

8. We use a _____ to measure things and draw lines. It is straight and is one foot long. It has 12 inches marked on it.

9. _____ come in many different colors. We draw, color, and write with them.

10. A _____ tells us the day, date, month, and year. It is usually on the wall.

> library   teacher   bathroom   chair   classroom
>
> computer   playground   map   student   bus

11. A _____ is a large place outside where students play. Recess usually happens here.

12. A _____ is a place where people go when they need to use the toilet. There are toilets, sinks, and sometimes mirrors.

13. A _____ is a room where teachers teach students. Students usually sit in chairs at desks or tables in this room.

14. A _____ is a piece of electronic equipment. People can type on the keyboard and use it for drawing, writing, playing games, and lots of other things.

15. A _____ is a piece of furniture that someone sits in. It usually has a back and four legs.

16. A _____ is a man or woman who teaches the class.

17. A _____ is a person in the class who studies and learns.

18. A _____ shows a drawing of a place or places. It usually shows cities, countries, mountains, rivers, and oceans.

19. A _____ is a place where we read and check out books.

20. A _____ is a large vehicle that picks children up and brings them to school. It also takes children home at the end of the day.

Activity 2: School Items

Holding up a picture of each item, have your students verbally supply the correct answer. (If students are advanced enough to read, they may circle the correct answers on their own.)

1. A student sits at this. It has a flat top for writing, drawing, and reading.

   What is it?   **desk**   **scissors**

2. This is a piece of electronic equipment. People can type on the keyboard and use it for drawing, writing, playing games, and lots of other things.

   What is it?   **calendar**   **computer**

3. This is a large vehicle that picks children up and brings them to school. It also takes children home at the end of the day.

   What is it?   **book**   **bus**

4. This is a book where notes are kept. It can have three rings or be spiral-bound.

   What is it?   **notebook**   **ruler**

5. We write on this. We can also cut it and make things with it. It is often white but can be other colors too.

   What is it?   **paper**   **map**

6. This is a person in the class who studies and learns.

   Who is it?   **teacher**   **student**

7. This shows a drawing of a place or places. It usually shows cities, countries, mountains, rivers, and oceans.

   What is it?   **chair**   **map**

8. This is usually made of wood and has an eraser. It needs to be sharpened. Students write with it.

   What is it?   **crayons**   **pencil**

9. This is a large place outside where students play. Recess usually happens here.

   What is it?   **playground**   **bathroom**

10. This is a room where teachers teach students. Students usually sit in chairs at desks or tables in this room.

    What is it?   **classroom**   **library**

11. We use these to cut paper and other things. They are usually made of metal and they are sharp.

    What are they?   **crayons**   **scissors**

12. This is a man or woman who teaches the class.

    Who is it?   **teacher**   **student**

13. This tells us the day, date, month, and year. It is usually on the wall.

    What is it?   **calendar**   **book**

14. This is a place where people go when they need to use the toilet. There are toilets, sinks, and sometimes mirrors.

    What is it?   **playground**   **bathroom**

15. This is a piece of furniture that someone sits in. It usually has a back and four legs.

    What is it?   **chair**   **computer**

16. This is something people read. It has pages and words. Sometimes it has pictures.

    What is it?   **book**   **pencil**

17. This is a piece of furniture that people sit around. It is flat and you can do a lot of things on it like read, write, color, and make things.

    What is it?   **map**   **table**

18. These come in many different colors. We draw, color, and write with them.

    What are they?   **scissors**   **crayons**

19. This is a place where we read and check out books.

    What is it?   **bathroom**   **library**

20. We use this to measure things and draw lines. It is straight and is one foot long. It has 12 inches marked on it.

    What is it?   **ruler**   **notebook**

Activity 3: School Items

Have your student read the story. Ask him to find each vocabulary word and circle it as he reads. Your student can use the word cards on page 56 as a reference. The story contains all 20 vocabulary words.

José was excited. Today he was going to take the bus to kindergarten. It was his first day of being a student! His new teacher was Mr. Wong. José's mother and father had given him a backpack with a notebook, pencils, erasers, and other new things for school. When the bus stopped at the school, José got out and found his classroom. It was near a nice playground that had swings and a slide. Inside the classroom, there was a desk and chair for each student. There were also tables with lots of things on them. Each table had paper, scissors, crayons, books, and rulers. There was a computer in one corner of the classroom and a map of the world on one wall.

Mr. Wong started class by having the students look at the calendar. They sat at their desks and talked about what day it was. Mr. Wong said that in a little while, after everybody had gone to the bathroom and had recess on the playground, they would visit the library and check out some books. José's day passed quickly. He couldn't believe it when the end of school came. He and the other students left their classroom and went to the bus to go home. José couldn't wait to tell his parents about his first day of school!

Optional Activities:

◆ Ask students to retell the story.
◆ Read the story out loud. Afterwards, ask questions about the story and have students provide answers. For example, "Why was José excited? What kinds of things did he see in his classroom?"
◆ After reading the story out loud, pick target vocabulary words out of the story and say each word phoneme by phoneme to allow students to practice sound blending. Example: "/D/-/e/-/s/-/k/; what word is that?" (Objective 15)
◆ Pick out a sentence and ask a student to count the number of words in the sentence. (Objective 11)
◆ Have students read the story silently or out loud to practice reading skills.
◆ After students are familiar with the story, read it out loud and omit the target vocabulary words. Have the students orally fill in the blanks.

Activity 4: School Items

Have your students complete these items to fulfill the listed objectives. Nonreading and nonwriting students can dictate the sentence while you transcribe it. (Objective 7)

1. Use the word *playground* in a sentence.

   _____

   _____

   How many words are in your sentence? _____

   How many syllables are in the word *playground*? _____

   How many sounds are in the word *playground*? _____

2. Use the word *desk* in a sentence.

   _____

   _____

   How many words are in your sentence? _____

   How many syllables are in the word *desk*? _____

   How many sounds are in the word *desk*? _____

3. Use the word *bathroom* in a sentence.

   _____

   _____

   How many words are in your sentence? _____

   How many syllables are in the word *bathroom*? _____

   How many sounds are in the word *bathroom*? _____

4. Use the word *crayons* in a sentence.

   _____

   _____

   How many words are in your sentence? _____

   How many syllables are in the word *crayons*? _____

   How many sounds are in the word *crayons*? _____

5. Use the word *library* in a sentence.

   _____

   _____

   How many words are in your sentence? _____

   How many syllables are in the word *library*? _____

   How many sounds are in the word *library*? _____

Activity 4: School Items, *continued*

6. Use the word *student* in a sentence.

_____

_____

How many words are in your sentence? _____

How many syllables are in the word *student*? _____

How many sounds are in the word *student*? _____

7. Use the word *scissors* in a sentence.

_____

_____

How many words are in your sentence? _____

How many syllables are in the word *scissors*? _____

How many sounds are in the word *scissors*? _____

8. Use the word *computer* in a sentence.

_____

_____

How many words are in your sentence? _____

How many syllables are in the word *computer*? _____

How many sounds are in the word *computer*? _____

9. Use the word *notebook* in a sentence.

_____

_____

How many words are in your sentence? _____

How many syllables are in the word *notebook*? _____

How many sounds are in the word *notebook*? _____

10. Use the word *map* in a sentence.

_____

_____

How many words are in your sentence? _____

How many syllables are in the word *map*? _____

How many sounds are in the word *map*? _____

11. Use the word *ruler* in a sentence.

_____

_____

      How many words are in your sentence?   _____

      How many syllables are in the word *ruler*?   _____

      How many sounds are in the word *ruler*?   _____

12. Use the word *classroom* in a sentence.

_____

_____

      How many words are in your sentence?   _____

      How many syllables are in the word *classroom*?   _____

      How many sounds are in the word *classroom*?   _____

13. Use the word *bus* in a sentence.

_____

_____

      How many words are in your sentence?   _____

      How many syllables are in the word *bus*?   _____

      How many sounds are in the word *bus*?   _____

14. Use the word *calendar* in a sentence.

_____

_____

      How many words are in your sentence?   _____

      How many syllables are in the word *calendar*?   _____

      How many sounds are in the word *calendar*?   _____

15. Use the word *book* in a sentence.

_____

_____

      How many words are in your sentence?   _____

      How many syllables are in the word *book*?   _____

      How many sounds are in the word *book*?   _____

Activity 4: School Items, *continued*

16. Use the word *table* in a sentence.

    _____

    _____

    How many words are in your sentence? _____
    How many syllables are in the word *table*? _____
    How many sounds are in the word *table*? _____

17. Use the word *paper* in a sentence.

    _____

    _____

    How many words are in your sentence? _____
    How many syllables are in the word *paper*? _____
    How many sounds are in the word *paper*? _____

18. Use the word *teacher* in a sentence.

    _____

    _____

    How many words are in your sentence? _____
    How many syllables are in the word *teacher*? _____
    How many sounds are in the word *teacher*? _____

19. Use the word *chair* in a sentence.

    _____

    _____

    How many words are in your sentence? _____
    How many syllables are in the word *chair*? _____
    How many sounds are in the word *chair*? _____

20. Use the word *pencil* in a sentence.

    _____

    _____

    How many words are in your sentence? _____
    How many syllables are in the word *pencil*? _____
    How many sounds are in the word *pencil*? _____

Activity 5: School Items

Have your students complete these items to fulfill the listed objective. Tell the students that some of these are silly, made-up words.

1. Circle the one that rhymes with *look*.

2. Circle the one that rhymes with *beecher*.

3. Circle the one that rhymes with *grable*.

4. Circle the one that rhymes with *tassroom*.

5. Circle the one that rhymes with *fuss*.

6. Circle the one that rhymes with *hair*.

7. Circle the one that rhymes with *mudent*.

8. Circle the one that rhymes with *sap*.

9. Circle the one that rhymes with *hayground*.

10. Circle the one that rhymes with *laper*.

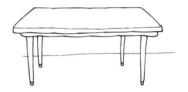

Activity 5: School Items, *continued*

11. Circle the one that rhymes with *snathroom*.

12. Circle the one that rhymes with *payons*.

13. Circle the one that rhymes with *cooler*.

14. Circle the one that rhymes with *dizzers*.

15. Circle the one that rhymes with *hotebook*.

16. Circle the one that rhymes with *resk*.

17. Circle the one that rhymes with *balendar*.

18. Circle the one that rhymes with *domputer*.

19. Circle the one that rhymes with *fencil*.

20. Circle the one that rhymes with *gibrary*.

Activity 6: School Items

Have your students complete these items to fulfill the listed objective.

Put an X on the picture when you hear its word said sound by sound. Say the word out loud.
(Example: /b/-/u/-/s/)

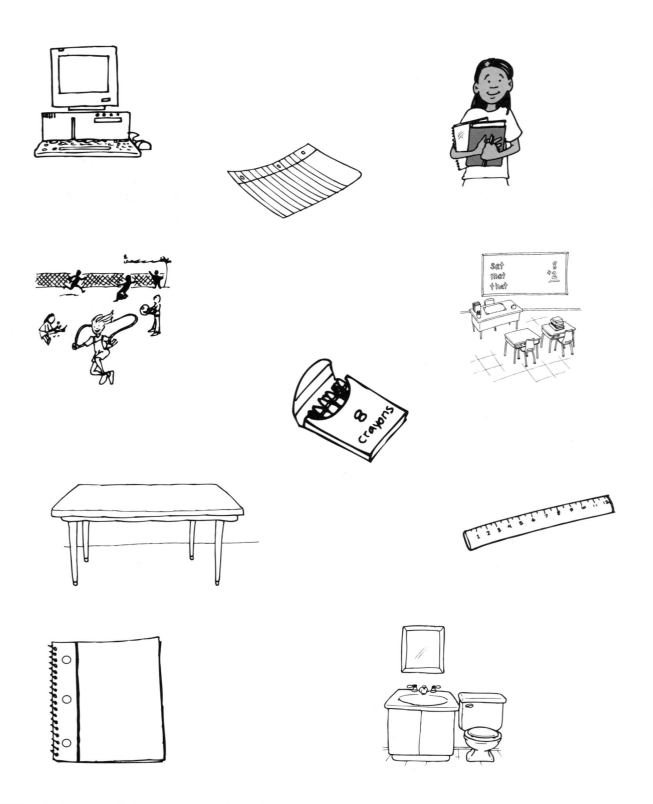

Activity 7: School Items

Have your students complete these items to fulfill the listed objectives. Read each word and then ask a question. Record each student's responses in the lines provided.

1. **teacher**

   What's the first sound in *teacher*? _____
   What's the last sound in *teacher*? _____
   How many syllables are in the word *teacher*? _____
   How many sounds are in the word *teacher*? _____

2. **playground**

   What's the first sound in *playground*? _____
   What's the last sound in *playground*? _____
   How many syllables are in the word *playground*? _____
   How many sounds are in the word *playground*? _____

3. **student**

   What's the first sound in *student*? _____
   What's the last sound in *student*? _____
   How many syllables are in the word *student*? _____
   How many sounds are in the word *student*? _____

4. **pencil**

   What's the first sound in *pencil*? _____
   What's the last sound in *pencil*? _____
   How many syllables are in the word *pencil*? _____
   How many sounds are in the word *pencil*? _____

5. **bathroom**

   What's the first sound in *bathroom*? _____
   What's the last sound in *bathroom*? _____
   How many syllables are in the word *bathroom*? _____
   How many sounds are in the word *bathroom*? _____

6. **book**

   What's the first sound in *book*? _____
   What's the last sound in *book*? _____
   How many syllables are in the word *book*? _____
   How many sounds are in the word *book*? _____

7. **crayons**

   What's the first sound in *crayons*? _____
   What's the last sound in *crayons*? _____
   How many syllables are in the word *crayons*? _____
   How many sounds are in the word *crayons*? _____

8. **chair**

What's the first sound in *chair*? _____
What's the last sound in *chair*? _____
How many syllables are in the word *chair*? _____
How many sounds are in the word *chair*? _____

9. **calendar**

What's the first sound in *calendar*? _____
What's the last sound in *calendar*? _____
How many syllables are in the word *calendar*? _____
How many sounds are in the word *calendar*? _____

10. **map**

What's the first sound in *map*? _____
What's the last sound in *map*? _____
How many syllables are in the word *map*? _____
How many sounds are in the word *map*? _____

11. **library**

What's the first sound in *library*? _____
What's the last sound in *library*? _____
How many syllables are in the word *library*? _____
How many sounds are in the word *library*? _____

12. **bus**

What's the first sound in *bus*? _____
What's the last sound in *bus*? _____
How many syllables are in the word *bus*? _____
How many sounds are in the word *bus*? _____

13. **classroom**

What's the first sound in *classroom*? _____
What's the last sound in *classroom*? _____
How many syllables are in the word *classroom*? _____
How many sounds are in the word *classroom*? _____

14. **desk**

What's the first sound in *desk*? _____
What's the last sound in *desk*? _____
How many syllables are in the word *desk*? _____
How many sounds are in the word *desk*? _____

15. **computer**

What's the first sound in *computer*? _____
What's the last sound in *computer*? _____
How many syllables are in the word *computer*? _____
How many sounds are in the word *computer*? _____

16. **table**

What's the first sound in *table*? _____
What's the last sound in *table*? _____
How many syllables are in the word *table*? _____
How many sounds are in the word *table*? _____

17. **scissors**

What's the first sound in *scissors*? _____
What's the last sound in *scissors*? _____
How many syllables are in the word *scissors*? _____
How many sounds are in the word *scissors*? _____

18. **notebook**

What's the first sound in *notebook*? _____
What's the last sound in *notebook*? _____
How many syllables are in the word *notebook*? _____
How many sounds are in the word *notebook*? _____

19. **paper**

What's the first sound in *paper*? _____
What's the last sound in *paper*? _____
How many syllables are in the word *paper*? _____
How many sounds are in the word *paper*? _____

20. **ruler**

What's the first sound in *ruler*? _____
What's the last sound in *ruler*? _____
How many syllables are in the word *ruler*? _____
How many sounds are in the word *ruler*? _____

Vocabulary Objectives

Annual Goal

Student will demonstrate increased receptive and expressive vocabulary skills.

Short-Term Objectives/Benchmarks

Objective 1

When the clinician verbally gives body part target vocabulary words, the student will point to pictures of these items with 80% accuracy.

Clinician: Sylvia, point to *eyes*. Point to *stomach*.
Student: (Points to each named picture.)

Objective 2

When the clinician holds up a picture and says, "Is this a(n) _____?" the student will verbally or nonverbally indicate *yes* or *no* with 80% accuracy.

Clinician: (Holds up a picture of *hands*.) Ming, are these *feet*?
Student: No. (Says verbally or shakes head *no*.)

Clinician: (Holds up a picture of a *mouth*.) Deirdre, is this a *mouth*?
Student: Yes. (Says verbally or shakes head *yes*.)

Objective 3

When the clinician gives a 1-2 sentence verbal description of a target word/concept and gives the student two choices of answers, the student will verbally supply the correct answer with 80% accuracy.

Clinician: Listen, Vera. This is something on our face. We smell things with it. Is it our *back* or our *nose*?
Student: Nose.

Objective 4

When shown pictures of body part target vocabulary words, the student will give verbal, one-word labels with 80% accuracy.

Clinician: (Shows picture of *feet*.) Gustavo, what are these?
Student: Feet.

75

Objective 5

When asked to verbally list 3-5 items in a given category, the student will do so with 80% accuracy.

Clinician: Josefina, tell me the names of four different body parts.
Student: Hands, stomach, eyes, knees.

Objective 6

When asked to define a target vocabulary word, the student will give a 5+ word verbal description with 80% accuracy.

Clinician: Angelo, what is a *mouth*?
Student: It is a part of our face that we smile and eat with.

Objective 7

When given a body part target vocabulary word, the student will use the word in a sentence with 80% accuracy.

Clinician: Raquel, please use the word *arms* in a sentence.
Student: We use our arms to carry things.

For more advanced students: (written language)

Objective 8

When presented with a paragraph or word list containing the body part target vocabulary word, the student will find and read the word out loud with 80% accuracy.

Clinician: Lubeya, look at this story. Please find the word *fingers*, and read the word to me after you find it.
Student: (Reads story.) Fingers. (Reads word aloud.)

Objective 9

When asked to spell a target vocabulary word, the student will spell the word out loud with 80% accuracy.

Clinician: Josef, please spell the word *face*.
Student: (Spells the word out loud.)

Objective 10

When given a target vocabulary word, the student will write a sentence containing the word with 80% accuracy.

Clinician: Kira, please write the word *hair* in a sentence.
Student: (Writes a sentence containing the word *hair*.)

Phonological Awareness Objectives

Annual Goal Student will demonstrate increased phonological awareness skills.

Short-Term Objectives/Benchmarks

Objective 11 With 80% accuracy, the student will count the number of words in a sentence that is prewritten or that the student has written.

Clinician: Look, Keesha. Here is a sentence in our story. Count how many words are in that sentence.
Student: (Counts the number of words in the sentence.)

Clinician: Daniel, you wrote a good sentence using the word *legs*. Please count how many words are in your sentence.
Student: (Counts the number of words in the sentence.)

Objective 12 When given a target vocabulary word, the student will identify the number of syllables in that word with 80% accuracy.

Clinician: Elize, how many syllables are in the word *stomach*?
Student: Two.

Objective 13 When given a target vocabulary word, the student will identify the number of sounds in that word with 80% accuracy.

Clinician: Tauili'il, how many sounds are in the word *back*?
Student: Three.

Objective 14 When the student hears a word that rhymes with a target vocabulary word, the student will identify that word verbally or nonverbally with 80% accuracy.

Clinician: Leonicio, color the picture that rhymes with *lace*.
Student: (Colors the picture of the face.)

Clinician: Bobby, what body part rhymes with *freeze*?
Student: Knees.

77

Objective *15*

When the student hears the speech pathologist say a target vocabulary word phoneme by phoneme, that student will demonstrate sound blending skills by stating the whole word with 80% accuracy.

Clinician: Casia, what word is this? /b/-/a/-/ck/
Student: Back.

Objective *16*

When given a target vocabulary word, the student will identify the first sound in that word upon request with 80% accuracy.

Clinician: Listen, Golda. *Toes.* What's the first sound in that word?
Student: /t/

Objective *17*

When given a target vocabulary word, the student will identify the last sound in that word upon request with 80% accuracy.

Clinician: Listen, Saphir. *Back.* What's the last sound in that word?
Student: /k/

Unit 2: Body Parts

Target Words	Objective 1 point to pictures		Objective 2 yes/no		Objective 3 2-choice answer		Objective 4 1-word label		Objective 5 list items		Objective 6 verbal definition	
Unit 2: Body Parts + Correct − Incorrect	Pretest Date	Posttest Date	Pretest Date	Posttest Date	Pretest Date	Posttest Date	Pretest Date	Posttest Date	Pretest Date	Posttest Date	Pretest Date	Posttest Date
1. arms												
2. back												
3. ears												
4. elbows												
5. eyes												
6. face												
7. feet												
8. fingers												
9. hair												
10. hands												
11. knees												
12. legs												
13. mouth												
14. neck												
15. nose												
16. stomach												
17. toes												
	% Correct	% Correct	% Correct	% Correct	% Correct	% Correct	% Correct	% Correct	% Correct	% Correct	% Correct	% Correct

Unit 2: Body Parts

Target Words Unit 2: Body Parts	Objective 7 say word in sentence		Objective 8 read word in paragraph		Objective 9 spell the word		Objective 10 write word in sentence		Objective 11 count words in sentence		Objective 12 count syllables in word	
+ Correct − Incorrect	Pretest Date	Posttest Date	Pretest Date	Posttest Date	Pretest Date	Posttest Date	Pretest Date	Posttest Date	Pretest Date	Posttest Date	Pretest Date	Posttest Date
1. arms												
2. back												
3. ears												
4. elbows												
5. eyes												
6. face												
7. feet												
8. fingers												
9. hair												
10. hands												
11. knees												
12. legs												
13. mouth												
14. neck												
15. nose												
16. stomach												
17. toes												
	% Correct	% Correct	% Correct	% Correct	% Correct	% Correct	% Correct	% Correct	% Correct	% Correct	% Correct	% Correct

Unit 2: Body Parts

Target Words	Objective 13		Objective 14		Objective 15		Objective 16		Objective 17	
Unit 2: Body Parts	identify number of sounds in word		identify rhyming word		sound blending		identify first sound in word		identify last sound in word	
+ Correct − Incorrect	Pretest Date	Posttest Date	Pretest Date	Posttest Date	Pretest Date	Posttest Date	Pretest Date	Posttest Date	Pretest Date	Posttest Date
1. arms										
2. back										
3. ears										
4. elbows										
5. eyes										
6. face										
7. feet										
8. fingers										
9. hair										
10. hands										
11. knees										
12. legs										
13. mouth										
14. neck										
15. nose										
16. stomach										
17. toes										
	% Correct	% Correct	% Correct	% Correct	% Correct	% Correct	% Correct	% Correct	% Correct	% Correct

Vocabulary Pictures: Cut these pictures apart to use in the activities that follow.

Vocabulary Pictures: Cut these pictures apart to use in the activities that follow.

There are many uses for these Word Cards, including having your students pair them with the picture cards, reading the words aloud (if students are able), or copying the words on the lines for practice. Use these vocabulary words in any way you see fit.

arms _____	back _____	ears _____
elbows _____	eyes _____	face _____
feet _____	fingers _____	hair _____
hands _____	knees _____	legs _____
mouth _____	neck _____	nose _____
stomach _____	toes _____	

Vocabulary Word Definitions

arms   We have two of these, one on either side of our body. We use them to carry things.

back   This is on the opposite side of our front. It has a backbone that helps us stand and sit.

ears   We hear with these. There is one on each side of our head.

elbows   These are in the middle of our arms. They are hard and we sometimes lean on them.

eyes   We have two of these on our face. We use them to see with.

face   This is the front part of our head. It has eyes, a nose, and a mouth.

feet   We have two of these. We put socks and shoes on them.

fingers   We have five of these on each hand. We use them to do lots of things, like writing.

hair   This grows on our head. It can be different colors, and it can be curly or straight.

hands   We have two of these, located at the ends of our arms. They have fingers attached to them.

knees   These are in the middle front part of our legs. They are hard and we can kneel on them.

legs   These have knees in the middle and feet at the end. They let us walk, run, and jump.

mouth   This is part of our face and has teeth inside it. We use it to smile and to eat.

neck   This holds up our head. It is between our head and our shoulders.

nose   This is in the middle of our face. We smell with it.

stomach   This is in the middle of the front of our body. When we eat, food goes here.

toes   We have five of these on the end of each foot. They help us to balance when we walk.

Activity 1: Body Parts

Have your students complete each definition with a word from the box. (Do this orally with nonreading students.)

eyes	arms	mouth	back
feet	stomach	hands	legs

1. We have two _____, one at the end of each leg. We put socks and shoes on them.

2. We have one _____. It is part of our face and has teeth inside it. We use it to smile and to eat.

3. Our _____ is in the middle of the front of our body. When we eat, food goes here.

4. We have two _____. They are a part our face, and we see with them.

5. We have two _____, one on either side of our body. We use them to carry things.

6. We have two _____. They have knees in the middle and feet at the end, and they let us walk, run, and jump.

7. We have two _____ at the ends of each of our arms. They have fingers attached to them.

8. Our _____ is on the opposite side of our front. It has a backbone that helps us stand and sit.

| neck | face | hair | elbows | nose |
| knees | ears | fingers | toes | |

9. We have two _____, one on each side of our head. We hear with these.

10. We have five _____ on the end of each foot. They help us to balance when we walk.

11. _____ grows on our head. It can be different colors, and it can be curly or straight.

12. Our _____ are in the middle of our arms. They are hard and we sometimes lean on them.

13. Our _____ is the front part of our head. It has eyes, a nose, and a mouth.

14. Our _____ holds up our head. It is between our head and our shoulders.

15. Our _____ are in the middle front part of our legs. They are hard and we can kneel on them.

16. We have one _____. It is in the middle of our face. We smell with it.

17. We have five _____ on each hand. We use them to do lots of things, like writing.

Activity 2: Body Parts

Holding up a picture of each item, have your students verbally supply the correct answer. (If students are advanced enough to read, they may circle the correct answers on their own.)

1. We have two of these, located at the ends of our arms. They have fingers attached to them.

   What are they? **toes** **hands**

2. This grows on our head. It can be different colors, and it can be curly or straight.

   What is it? **stomach** **hair**

3. We have two of these on our face. We see with them.

   What are they? **eyes** **elbows**

4. We have two of these, one on either side of our body. We use them to carry things.

   What are they? **ears** **arms**

5. This holds up our head. It is between our head and our shoulders.

   What is it? **neck** **mouth**

6. This is the front part of our head. It has eyes, a nose, and a mouth.

   What is it? **feet** **face**

7. This is in the middle of the front of our body. When we eat, food goes here.

   What is it? **neck** **stomach**

8. These have knees in the middle and feet at the end. They let us walk, run, and jump.

   What are they? **fingers** **legs**

9. This is in the middle of our face. We smell with it.

   What is it? **nose** **back**

10. We have five of these on the end of each foot. They help us to balance when we walk.

    What are they? **ears** **toes**

11. This is part of our face and has teeth inside it. We use it to smile and to eat.

    What is it?   **mouth**   **neck**

12. We hear with these. There is one on each side of our head.

    What are they?   **elbows**   **ears**

13. These are in the middle front part of our legs. They are hard and we can kneel on them.

    What are they?   **knees**   **fingers**

14. We have two of these. We put socks and shoes on them.

    What are they?   **feet**   **hands**

15. This is on the opposite side of our front. It has a backbone that helps us stand and sit.

    What is it?   **back**   **face**

16. We have five of these on each hand. We use them to do lots of things, like writing.

    What are they?   **fingers**   **eyes**

17. These are in the middle of our arms. They are hard and we sometimes lean on them.

    What are they?   **legs**   **elbows**

Activity 3: Body Parts

Have your student read the story. Ask him to find each vocabulary word and circle it as he reads. Your student can use the word cards on page 84 as a reference. The story contains all 17 vocabulary words.

Maya was taking a bath. She had been out playing in the dirt and her hands and knees were very dirty. She even had dirt all over her face! Maya's elbows were dirty too, and she had mud on her legs and feet. When Maya's mother brought her into the house, she told Maya that she would have to wash her hair too. Maya had been having fun playing outside!

When Maya's mother washed her hair, she said, "Close your eyes, and I will try to keep the shampoo off of your face." So Maya closed her eyes, but she started talking and some shampoo accidentally got into her mouth. That didn't taste very good! But Maya's nose told her the shampoo smelled good, and she asked if she could use her fingers to help her mother wash her hair. Maya's mother said, "OK," and Maya lifted up her arms to help her mother wash her hair. She rubbed some shampoo on her neck, which had gotten dirty too. A little shampoo got into her ears, but that didn't hurt. "OK," said Maya's mother, "you are looking a lot cleaner. But let's not forget to wash your back and stomach." When Maya was all done with her bath, she looked clean and smelled good. Her mother even let her put some cream on her feet, legs, toes, and hands. Maya was so clean that she decided to wait a few days before she played in the dirt again!

Optional Activities:

◆ Ask students to retell the story.
◆ Read the story out loud. Afterwards, ask questions about the story and have students provide answers. For example, "Why was Maya taking a bath? What parts of her body did her mother help her wash?"
◆ After reading the story out loud, pick target vocabulary words out of the story and say each word phoneme by phoneme to allow students to practice sound blending. Example: "/F/-/ee/-/t/; what word is that?" (Objective 15)
◆ Pick out a sentence and ask a student to count the number of words in the sentence. (Objective 11)
◆ Have students read the story silently or out loud to practice reading skills.
◆ After students are familiar with the story, read it out loud and omit the target vocabulary words. Have the students orally fill in the blanks.

Activity 4: Body Parts

Have your students complete these items to fulfill the listed objectives. Nonreading and nonwriting students can dictate the sentence while you transcribe it. (Objective 7)

1. Use the word *neck* in a sentence.

   _____

   _____

   How many words are in your sentence? _____
   How many syllables are in the word *neck*? _____
   How many sounds are in the word *neck*? _____

2. Use the word *elbows* in a sentence.

   _____

   _____

   How many words are in your sentence? _____
   How many syllables are in the word *elbows*? _____
   How many sounds are in the word *elbows*? _____

3. Use the word *mouth* in a sentence.

   _____

   _____

   How many words are in your sentence? _____
   How many syllables are in the word *mouth*? _____
   How many sounds are in the word *mouth*? _____

4. Use the word *hair* in a sentence.

   _____

   _____

   How many words are in your sentence? _____
   How many syllables are in the word *hair*? _____
   How many sounds are in the word *hair*? _____

5. Use the word *hands* in a sentence.

   _____

   _____

   How many words are in your sentence? _____
   How many syllables are in the word *hands*? _____
   How many sounds are in the word *hands*? _____

Activity 4: Body Parts, *continued*

6. Use the word *stomach* in a sentence.

_____

_____

       How many words are in your sentence?   _____

       How many syllables are in the word *stomach*?   _____

       How many sounds are in the word *stomach*?   _____

7. Use the word *knees* in a sentence.

_____

_____

       How many words are in your sentence?   _____

       How many syllables are in the word *knees*?   _____

       How many sounds are in the word *knees*?   _____

8. Use the word *fingers* in a sentence.

_____

_____

       How many words are in your sentence?   _____

       How many syllables are in the word *fingers*?   _____

       How many sounds are in the word *fingers*?   _____

9. Use the word *nose* in a sentence.

_____

_____

       How many words are in your sentence?   _____

       How many syllables are in the word *nose*?   _____

       How many sounds are in the word *nose*?   _____

10. Use the word *face* in a sentence.

_____

_____

       How many words are in your sentence?   _____

       How many syllables are in the word *face*?   _____

       How many sounds are in the word *face*?   _____

11. Use the word *back* in a sentence.

_____

_____

       How many words are in your sentence?   _____

       How many syllables are in the word *back*?   _____

       How many sounds are in the word *back*?   _____

12. Use the word *eyes* in a sentence.

_____

_____

How many words are in your sentence?   _____

How many syllables are in the word *eyes*?   _____

How many sounds are in the word *eyes*?   _____

13. Use the word *legs* in a sentence.

_____

_____

How many words are in your sentence?   _____

How many syllables are in the word *legs*?   _____

How many sounds are in the word *legs*?   _____

14. Use the word *toes* in a sentence.

_____

_____

How many words are in your sentence?   _____

How many syllables are in the word *toes*?   _____

How many sounds are in the word *toes*?   _____

15. Use the word *feet* in a sentence.

_____

_____

How many words are in your sentence?   _____

How many syllables are in the word *feet*?   _____

How many sounds are in the word *feet*?   _____

16. Use the word *ears* in a sentence.

_____

_____

How many words are in your sentence?   _____

How many syllables are in the word *ears*?   _____

How many sounds are in the word *ears*?   _____

17. Use the word *arms* in a sentence.

_____

_____

How many words are in your sentence?   _____

How many syllables are in the word *arms*?   _____

How many sounds are in the word *arms*?   _____

Activity 5: Body Parts

Have your students complete these items to fulfill the listed objective. Tell the students that some of these are silly, made-up words.

1. Circle the one that rhymes with *hose*.

2. Circle the one that rhymes with *begs*.

3. Circle the one that rhymes with *telbows*.

4. Circle the one that rhymes with *share*.

5. Circle the one that rhymes with *south*.

6. Circle the one that rhymes with *deck*.

7. Circle the one that rhymes with *gears*.

8. Circle the one that rhymes with *farms*.

9. Circle the one that rhymes with *bingers*.

10. Circle the one that rhymes with *meet*.

11. Circle the one that rhymes with *chomach*.

12. Circle the one that rhymes with *sack*.

13. Circle the one that rhymes with *freeze*.

14. Circle the one that rhymes with *sands*.

15. Circle the one that rhymes with *rose*.

16. Circle the one that rhymes with *race*.

17. Circle the one that rhymes with *prize*.

Activity 6: Body Parts

Have your students complete these items to fulfill the listed objective.

Put an X on the picture when you hear its word said sound by sound. Say the word out loud.
(Example: /n/-/e/-/ck/)

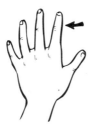

Activity 7: Body Parts

Objectives 12, 13, 16, 17

Have your students complete these items to fulfill the listed objectives. Read each word and then ask a question. Record each student's responses in the lines provided.

1. **eyes**

   What's the first sound in *eyes*? _____
   What's the last sound in *eyes*? _____
   How many syllables are in the word *eyes*? _____
   How many sounds are in the word *eyes*? _____

2. **face**

   What's the first sound in *face*? _____
   What's the last sound in *face*? _____
   How many syllables are in the word *face*? _____
   How many sounds are in the word *face*? _____

3. **neck**

   What's the first sound in *neck*? _____
   What's the last sound in *neck*? _____
   How many syllables are in the word *neck*? _____
   How many sounds are in the word *neck*? _____

4. **hands**

   What's the first sound in *hands*? _____
   What's the last sound in *hands*? _____
   How many syllables are in the words *hands*? _____
   How many sounds are in the words *hands*? _____

5. **knees**

   What's the first sound in *knees*? _____
   What's the last sound in *knees*? _____
   How many syllables are in the word *knees*? _____
   How many sounds are in the word *knees*? _____

6. **back**

   What's the first sound in *back*? _____
   What's the last sound in *back*? _____
   How many syllables are in the word *back*? _____
   How many sounds are in the word *back*? _____

7. **nose**

What's the first sound in *nose*? _____
What's the last sound in *nose*? _____
How many syllables are in the word *nose*? _____
How many sounds are in the word *nose*? _____

8. **arms**

What's the first sound in *arms*? _____
What's the last sound in *arms*? _____
How many syllables are in the word *arms*? _____
How many sounds are in the word *arms*? _____

9. **fingers**

What's the first sound in *fingers*? _____
What's the last sound in *fingers*? _____
How many syllables are in the word *fingers*? _____
How many sounds are in the word *fingers*? _____

10. **feet**

What's the first sound in *feet*? _____
What's the last sound in *feet*? _____
How many syllables are in the word *feet*? _____
How many sounds are in the word *feet*? _____

11. **stomach**

What's the first sound in *stomach*? _____
What's the last sound in *stomach*? _____
How many syllables are in the word *stomach*? _____
How many sounds are in the word *stomach*? _____

12. **mouth**

What's the first sound in *mouth*? _____
What's the last sound in *mouth*? _____
How many syllables are in the word *mouth*? _____
How many sounds are in the word *mouth*? _____

13. **hair**

What's the first sound in *hair*? _____
What's the last sound in *hair*? _____
How many syllables are in the word *hair*? _____
How many sounds are in the word *hair*? _____

14. **elbows**

   What's the first sound in *elbows*? _____
   What's the last sound in *elbows*? _____
   How many syllables are in the word *elbows*? _____
   How many sounds are in the word *elbows*? _____

15. **legs**

   What's the first sound in *legs*? _____
   What's the last sound in *legs*? _____
   How many syllables are in the word *legs*? _____
   How many sounds are in the word *legs*? _____

16. **toes**

   What's the first sound in *toes*? _____
   What's the last sound in *toes*? _____
   How many syllables are in the word *toes*? _____
   How many sounds are in the word *toes*? _____

17. **ears**

   What's the first sound in *ears*? _____
   What's the last sound in *ears*? _____
   How many syllables are in the word *ears*? _____
   How many sounds are in the word *ears*? _____

Vocabulary Objectives

 **Annual Goal** Student will demonstrate increased receptive and expressive vocabulary skills.

Short-Term Objectives/Benchmarks

Objective 1

When the clinician verbally gives food item vocabulary words, the student will point to pictures of these items with 80% accuracy.

Clinician: Juan, point to *apple*. Point to *sandwich*.
Student: (Points to each named picture.)

Objective 2

When the clinician holds up a picture and says, "Is this a(n) _____?" the student will verbally or nonverbally indicate *yes* or *no* with 80% accuracy.

Clinician: (Holds up a picture of *milk*.) Mazar, is this *cheese*?
Student: No. (Says verbally or shakes head *no.*)

Clinician: (Holds up a picture of *ice cream*.) Christina, is this *ice cream*?
Student: Yes. (Says verbally or shakes head *yes.*)

Objective 3

When the clinician gives a 1-2 sentence verbal description of a target word/concept and gives the student two choices of answers, the student will verbally supply the correct answer with 80% accuracy.

Clinician: Listen, Phong. This is purple and it is a fruit. It comes in bunches and is sweet. Is it *grapes* or *cherries*?
Student: Grapes.

Objective 4

When shown pictures of food item target vocabulary words, the student will give verbal, one-word labels with 80% accuracy.

Clinician: (Shows picture of a *tomato*.) Samuel, what's this?
Student: Tomato.

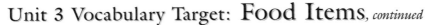

Objective 5 When asked to verbally list 3-5 items in a given category, the student will do so with 80% accuracy.

Clinician: Rodrigo, tell me the names of four different foods.
Student: Grapes, cheese, ice cream, orange.

Objective 6 When asked to define a target vocabulary word, the student will give a 5+ word verbal description with 80% accuracy.

Clinician: Tran, what is a *sandwich*?
Student: It is two slices of bread and something in the middle.

Objective 7 When given a food item target vocabulary word, the student will use the word in a sentence with 80% accuracy.

Clinician: Maria, please use the word *carrot* in a sentence.
Student: A carrot is orange and it's a vegetable.

For more advanced students: (written language)

Objective 8 When presented with a paragraph or word list containing the food item target vocabulary word, the student will find and read the word out loud with 80% accuracy.

Clinician: Ginny, look at this story. Please find the word *potato*, and read the word to me after you find it.
Student: (Reads story.) Potato. (Reads word aloud.)

Objective 9 When asked to spell a target vocabulary word, the student will spell the word out loud with 80% accuracy.

Clinician: Jaime, please spell the word *hamburger*.
Student: (Spells the word out loud.)

Objective 10 When given a target vocabulary word, the student will write a sentence containing the word with 80% accuracy.

Clinician: Eva, please write the word *butter* in a sentence.
Student: (Writes a sentence containing the word *butter*.)

Phonological Awareness Objectives

Annual Goal

Student will demonstrate increased phonological awareness skills.

Short-Term Objectives/Benchmarks

Objective 11
With 80% accuracy, the student will count the number of words in a sentence that is prewritten or that the student has written.

Clinician: Look, Carol. Here is a sentence in our story. Count how many words are in that sentence.
Student: (Counts the number of words in the sentence.)

Clinician: Lee, you wrote a good sentence using the word *tomato*. Please count how many words are in your sentence.
Student: (Counts the number of words in the sentence.)

Objective 12
When given a target vocabulary word, the student will identify the number of syllables in that word with 80% accuracy.

Clinician: Ritchie, how many syllables are in the word *hamburger*?
Student: Three.

Objective 13
When given a target vocabulary word, the student will identify the number of sounds in that word with 80% accuracy.

Clinician: Marnes, how many sounds are in the word *butter*?
Student: Four.

Objective 14
When the student hears a word that rhymes with a target vocabulary word, the student will identify that word verbally or nonverbally with 80% accuracy.

Clinician: Katja, color the picture that rhymes with *tease*.
Student: (Colors the picture of the cheese.)

Clinician: Nicholas, what food rhymes with *leg*?
Student: Egg.

Objective 15 When the student hears the speech pathologist say a target vocabulary word phoneme by phoneme, that student will demonstrate sound blending skills by stating the whole word with 80% accuracy.

Clinician: Tony, what word is this? /b/-/u/tt/-/er/

Student: Butter.

Objective 16 When given a target vocabulary word, the student will identify the first sound in that word upon request with 80% accuracy.

Clinician: Listen, Mikaih. *Hamburger*. What's the first sound in that word?

Student: /h/

Objective 17 When given a target vocabulary word, the student will identify the last sound in that word upon request with 80% accuracy.

Clinician: Listen, Lucy. *Hamburger*. What's the last sound in that word?

Student: /r/

Unit 3: Food Items

Target Words Unit 3: Food Items + Correct − Incorrect	Objective 1 point to pictures Pretest Date	Objective 1 Posttest Date	Objective 2 yes/no Pretest Date	Objective 2 Posttest Date	Objective 3 2-choice answer Pretest Date	Objective 3 Posttest Date	Objective 4 1-word label Pretest Date	Objective 4 Posttest Date	Objective 5 list items Pretest Date	Objective 5 Posttest Date	Objective 6 verbal definition Pretest Date	Objective 6 Posttest Date
1. apple												
2. banana												
3. bread												
4. butter												
5. carrot												
6. cheese												
7. cherries												
8. corn												
9. egg												
10. French fries												
11. grapes												
12. hamburger												
13. hot dog												
14. ice cream												
15. lemon												
16. lettuce												
17. orange												
18. potato												
19. sandwich												
20. tomato												
% Correct	% Correct		% Correct	% Correct	% Correct	% Correct	% Correct	% Correct	% Correct	% Correct	% Correct	% Correct

Unit 3: Food Items

Target Words	Objective 7 say word in sentence		Objective 8 read word in paragraph		Objective 9 spell the word		Objective 10 write word in sentence		Objective 11 count words in sentence		Objective 12 count syllables in word	
Unit 3: Food Items	Pretest Date	Posttest Date	Pretest Date	Posttest Date	Pretest Date	Posttest Date	Pretest Date	Posttest Date	Pretest Date	Posttest Date	Pretest Date	Posttest Date
+ Correct – Incorrect												
1. apple												
2. banana												
3. bread												
4. butter												
5. carrot												
6. cheese												
7. cherries												
8. corn												
9. egg												
10. French fries												
11. grapes												
12. hamburger												
13. hot dog												
14. ice cream												
15. lemon												
16. lettuce												
17. orange												
18. potato												
19. sandwich												
20. tomato												
	% Correct	% Correct	% Correct	% Correct	% Correct	% Correct	% Correct	% Correct	% Correct	% Correct	% Correct	% Correct

Unit 3: Food Items

Target Words Unit 3: Food Items	Objective 13 identify number of sounds in word		Objective 14 identify rhyming word		Objective 15 sound blending		Objective 16 identify first sound in word		Objective 17 identify last sound in word	
+ Correct − Incorrect	Pretest Date	Posttest Date	Pretest Date	Posttest Date	Pretest Date	Posttest Date	Pretest Date	Posttest Date	Pretest Date	Posttest Date
1. apple										
2. banana										
3. bread										
4. butter										
5. carrot										
6. cheese										
7. cherries										
8. corn										
9. egg										
10. French fries										
11. grapes										
12. hamburger										
13. hot dog										
14. ice cream										
15. lemon										
16. lettuce										
17. orange										
18. potato										
19. sandwich										
20. tomato										
	% Correct	% Correct	% Correct	% Correct	% Correct	% Correct	% Correct	% Correct	% Correct	% Correct

Vocabulary Pictures: Cut these pictures apart to use in the activities that follow.

Vocabulary Pictures: Cut these pictures apart to use in the activities that follow.

There are many uses for these Word Cards, including having your students pair them with the picture cards, reading the words aloud (if students are able), or copying the words on the lines for practice. Use these vocabulary words in any way you see fit.

apple	banana	bread
butter	carrot	cheese
cherries	corn	egg
French fries	grapes	hamburger
hot dog	ice cream	lemon
lettuce	orange	potato
sandwich	tomato	

Vocabulary Word Definitions

apple	A small, red, crunchy fruit that grows on trees.
banana	A long yellow fruit with a skin that you peel off.
bread	A soft food made from dough. It often comes in loaves.
butter	A dairy product that is usually yellow. We often spread it on our bread.
carrot	An orange, crunchy vegetable that is long and pointed at the end.
cheese	A dairy product made from milk. We sometimes put it on our sandwiches.
cherries	Small, round, juicy, red fruits with seeds in the middle and stems on top.
corn	A yellow vegetable that grows on cobs.
egg	A food that is laid by chickens. It is oval-shaped and has a yellow yolk in the center.
French fries	Strips of potato that have been fried. We often eat them with hamburgers.
grapes	Small, round, sweet, juicy fruits that can be purple or green. They grow in bunches.
hamburger	A small, round, cooked meat patty that is usually served inside a bun. We often put mustard and ketchup on this.
hot dog	A wiener usually served hot in a long, soft bread roll. We sometimes put ketchup, mustard, relish, or onions on this.
ice cream	A cold, sweet dessert that we usually eat on cones or in bowls.
lemon	A small, sour, yellow citrus fruit that grows on trees.
lettuce	A green, leafy, crunchy vegetable that we use in salads.
orange	A round, orange-colored, sweet juicy fruit that grows on trees.
potato	A brown vegetable that grows in the ground. It can be eaten in lots of ways — baked, fried, mashed, or boiled.
sandwich	Made of two pieces of bread with foods like cheese in the middle.
tomato	A red, juicy vegetable with seeds in the middle. It is round and soft on the outside.

Activity 1: Food Items

Have your students complete each definition with a word from the box. (Do this orally with nonreading students.)

hot dog	ice cream	bread	French fries	butter
sandwich	apple	cheese	egg	hamburger

1. A _____ is a small, round, cooked meat patty that is usually served inside a bun. We often put mustard and ketchup on this.

2. A _____ is a wiener usually served hot in a long, soft bread roll. We sometimes put ketchup, mustard, relish, or onions on this.

3. _____ are strips of potato that have been fried. We often eat them with hamburgers.

4. _____ is a cold, sweet dessert that we usually eat on cones or in bowls.

5. An _____ is a food that is laid by chickens. It is oval-shaped and has a yellow yolk in the center.

6. _____ is a dairy product made from milk. We sometimes put it on our sandwiches.

7. A _____ is made of two pieces of bread with foods like cheese in the middle.

8. _____ is a soft food made from dough. It often comes in loaves.

9. _____ is a dairy product that is usually yellow. We often spread it on our bread.

10. An _____ is a small, red, crunchy fruit that grows on trees.

lettuce	banana	grapes	potato	corn
orange	carrot	tomato	cherries	lemon

11. _____ are small, round, sweet, juicy fruits that can be purple or green. They grow in bunches.

12. An _____ is a round, orange-colored, sweet juicy fruit that grows on trees.

13. _____ are small, round juicy, red fruits with seeds in the middle and stems on top.

14. A _____ is a long yellow fruit with a skin that you peel off.

15. A _____ is a small, sour, yellow citrus fruit that grows on trees.

16. _____ is a green, leafy, crunchy vegetable that we use in salads.

17. A _____ is a red, juicy vegetable with seeds in the middle. It is round and soft on the outside.

18. _____ is a yellow vegetable that grows on cobs.

19. A _____ is an orange, crunchy vegetable that is long and pointed at the end.

20. A _____ is a brown vegetable that grows in the ground. It can be eaten in lots of ways — baked, fried, mashed, or boiled.

Activity 2: Food Items

Holding up a picture of each item, have your students verbally supply the correct answer. (If students are advanced enough to read, they may circle the correct answers on their own.)

1. This is a small, round, cooked meat patty that is usually served inside a bun.

   What is it? **tomato** **hamburger**

2. This is a food that is laid by chickens. It is oval-shaped and has a yellow yolk in the center.

   What is it? **potato** **egg**

3. This is a red, juicy vegetable with seeds in the middle. It is round and soft on the outside.

   What is it? **corn** **tomato**

4. This is an orange, crunchy vegetable that is long and pointed at the end.

   What is it? **corn** **carrot**

5. This is a small, red, crunchy fruit that grows on trees.

   What is it? **apple** **tomato**

6. This is a dairy product that is usually yellow. We often spread it on our bread.

   What is it? **lemon** **butter**

7. This is a round, orange-colored, sweet, juicy fruit that grows on trees.

   What is it? **orange** **potato**

8. This is a dairy product made from milk. We sometimes put it on our sandwiches.

   What is it? **hot dog** **cheese**

9. This is a long yellow fruit with skin that you peel off.

   What is it? **banana** **bread**

10. This is a cold, sweet dessert that we usually eat on cones or in bowls.

    What is it? **egg** **ice cream**

11. These are strips of potato that have been fried. We often eat them with hamburgers.

    What are they? **French fries** **cherries**

114

12. This is a small, sour, yellow citrus fruit that grows on trees.

    What is it?   **lettuce**   **lemon**

13. This is a wiener usually served hot on a long, soft bread roll.

    What is it?   **orange**   **hot dog**

14. These are small, round, sweet, juicy fruits that can be purple or green. They grow in bunches.

    What are they?   **carrots**   **grapes**

15. This is a soft food made from dough. It often comes in loaves.

    What is it?   **bread**   **lettuce**

16. This is a yellow vegetable that grows on cobs.

    What is it?   **corn**   **egg**

17. This is a green, leafy, crunchy vegetable that we use in salads.

    What is it?   **lettuce**   **corn**

18. These are small, round, juicy, red fruits with seeds in the middle and stems on top.

    What are they?   **cherries**   **lemons**

19. This is made of two pieces of bread with foods like cheese in the middle.

    What is it?   **ice cream**   **sandwich**

20. This is a brown vegetable that grows in the ground. It can be eaten in lots of ways — baked, fried, mashed, or boiled.

    What is it?   **potato**   **butter**

Activity 3: Food Items

Have your student read the story. Ask him to find each vocabulary word and circle it as he reads. Your student can use the word cards on page 110 as a reference. The story contains all 20 vocabulary words.

Dad and the kids were going shopping for groceries on Saturday morning. Mom said, "Be sure to remember cheese! And don't forget to pick up hamburgers for lunch on the way home!"

Dad and the kids piled into the car. Jaime asked, "Did we forget to put eggs on the list?" "No," Dad said, "but will you please write down hot dogs? I forgot that one!" "We need ice cream," said Maria, "because Grandma is coming tonight. We want this to be special!"

Finally the family arrived at the store. "OK," said Dad, "let's split up. Jaime, you take Benjamin and find the vegetables. Remember, for our vegetable soup tonight, we will need carrots, a tomato, corn, and a potato. Also, get lettuce for a salad. Maria, you need to get the fruit. We need apples, bananas, grapes, oranges, lemons, and cherries. "Hey, Dad!" Jaime exclaimed. "What are you going to buy?" "Why, I'll purchase the rest of the items on the list," Dad told him. "I have to find bread and butter if we want sandwiches for lunch next week. I'll also get hot dogs."

Dad and the kids had a great time at the grocery store. They got hamburgers and French fries on the way home. And when they got home, Mom thanked them for buying the groceries!

Optional Activities:

♦ Ask students to retell the story.

♦ Read the story out loud. Afterwards, ask questions about the story and have students provide answers. For example, "Who was coming tonight? List four kinds of vegetables that they bought. What did they get on the way home?"

♦ After reading the story out loud, pick target vocabulary words out of the story and say each word phoneme by phoneme to allow students to practice sound blending. Example: "/M/-/i/-/l/-/k/; what word is that?" (Objective 15)

♦ Pick out a sentence and ask a student to count the number of words in the sentence. (Objective 11)

♦ Have students read the story silently or out loud to practice reading skills.

♦ After students are familiar with the story, read it out loud and omit the target vocabulary words. Have the students orally fill in the blanks.

Activity 4: Food Items

Have your students complete these items to fulfill the listed objectives. Nonreading and nonwriting students can dictate the sentence while you transcribe it. (Objective 7)

1. Use the word *hamburger* in a sentence.

   _____

   _____

   How many words are in your sentence? _____

   How many syllables are in the word *hamburger*? _____

   How many sounds are in the word *hamburger*? _____

2. Use the words *hot dog* in a sentence.

   _____

   _____

   How many words are in your sentence? _____

   How many syllables are in the words *hot dog*? _____

   How many sounds are in the words *hot dog*? _____

3. Use the word *egg* in a sentence.

   _____

   _____

   How many words are in your sentence? _____

   How many syllables are in the word *egg*? _____

   How many sounds are in the word *egg*? _____

4. Use the words *ice cream* in a sentence.

   _____

   _____

   How many words are in your sentence? _____

   How many syllables are in the words *ice cream*? _____

   How many sounds are in the words *ice cream*? _____

5. Use the word *cheese* in a sentence.

   _____

   _____

   How many words are in your sentence? _____

   How many syllables are in the word *cheese*? _____

   How many sounds are in the word *cheese*? _____

Activity 4: Food Items, *continued*

6. Use the word *potato* in a sentence.

   _____

   _____

   How many words are in your sentence?   _____

   How many syllables are in the word *potato*?   _____

   How many sounds are in the word *potato*?   _____

7. Use the word *sandwich* in a sentence.

   _____

   _____

   How many words are in your sentence?   _____

   How many syllables are in the word *sandwich*? _____

   How many sounds are in the word *sandwich*?   _____

8. Use the word *bread* in a sentence.

   _____

   _____

   How many words are in your sentence?   _____

   How many syllables are in the word *bread*?   _____

   How many sounds are in the word *bread*?   _____

9. Use the word *butter* in a sentence.

   _____

   _____

   How many words are in your sentence?   _____

   How many syllables are in the word *butter*?   _____

   How many sounds are in the word *butter*?   _____

10. Use the word *apple* in a sentence.

   _____

   _____

   How many words are in your sentence?   _____

   How many syllables are in the word *apple*?   _____

   How many sounds are in the word *apple*?   _____

11. Use the word *grapes* in a sentence.

_____

_____

     How many words are in your sentence? _____

     How many syllables are in the word *grapes*? _____

     How many sounds are in the word *grapes*? _____

12. Use the word *orange* in a sentence.

_____

_____

     How many words are in your sentence? _____

     How many syllables are in the word *orange*? _____

     How many sounds are in the word *orange*? _____

13. Use the word *cherries* in a sentence.

_____

_____

     How many words are in your sentence? _____

     How many syllables are in the word *cherries*? _____

     How many sounds are in the word *cherries*? _____

14. Use the word *banana* in a sentence.

_____

_____

     How many words are in your sentence? _____

     How many syllables are in the word *banana*? _____

     How many sounds are in the word *banana*? _____

15. Use the word *lemon* in a sentence.

_____

_____

     How many words are in your sentence? _____

     How many syllables are in the word *lemon*? _____

     How many sounds are in the word *lemon*? _____

Activity 4: Food Items, *continued*

16. Use the word *lettuce* in a sentence.

_____

_____

How many words are in your sentence?   _____

How many syllables are in the word *lettuce*?   _____

How many sounds are in the word *lettuce*?   _____

17. Use the word *tomato* in a sentence.

_____

_____

How many words are in your sentence?   _____

How many syllables are in the word *tomato*?   _____

How many sounds are in the word *tomato*?   _____

18. Use the word *corn* in a sentence.

_____

_____

How many words are in your sentence?   _____

How many syllables are in the word *corn*?   _____

How many sounds are in the word *corn*?   _____

19. Use the word *carrot* in a sentence.

_____

_____

How many words are in your sentence?   _____

How many syllables are in the word *carrot*?   _____

How many sounds are in the word *carrot*?   _____

20. Use the words *French fries* in a sentence.

_____

_____

How many words are in your sentence?   _____

How many syllables are in the words *French fries*?   _____

How many sounds are in the words *French fries*?   _____

Activity 5: Food Items

Have your students complete these items to fulfill the listed objective. Tell the students that some of these are silly, made-up words.

1. Circle the one that rhymes with *torn*.

2. Circle the one that rhymes with *head*.

3. Circle the one that rhymes with *cutter*.

4. Circle the one that rhymes with *tease*.

5. Circle the one that rhymes with *smotdog*.

6. Circle the one that rhymes with *Pench pies*.

7. Circle the one that rhymes with *Snapple*.

8. Circle the one that rhymes with *leg*.

9. Circle the one that rhymes with *handwich*.

10. Circle the one that rhymes with *berries*.

121

Activity 5: Food Items, *continued*

11. Circle the one that rhymes with *lomato*.

12. Circle the one that rhymes with *tamburger*.

13. Circle the one that rhymes with *kice dream*.

14. Circle the one that rhymes with *rettuce*.

15. Circle the one that rhymes with *parrot*.

16. Circle the one that rhymes with *botato*.

17. Circle the one that rhymes with *crapes*.

18. Circle the one that rhymes with *fanana*.

19. Circle the one that rhymes with *borange*.

20. Circle the one that rhymes with *chemon*.

Activity 6: Food Items

Have your students complete these items to fulfill the listed objective.

Put an X on the picture when you hear its word said letter by letter. Say the word out loud.
(Example: /l/-/e/-/m/-/o/-/n/)

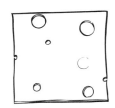

Activity 7: Food Items

Have your students complete these items to fulfill the listed
objectives. Read each word and then ask a question. Record
each student's responses in the lines provided.

1. **hamburger**

   What's the first sound in *hamburger*? _____
   What's the last sound in *hamburger*? _____
   How many syllables are in the word *hamburger*? _____
   How many sounds are in the word *hamburger*? _____

2. **hot dog**

   What's the first sound in *hot dog*? _____
   What's the last sound in *hot dog*? _____
   How many syllables are in the words *hot dog* _____
   How many sounds are in the words *hot dog*? _____

3. **egg**

   What's the first sound in *egg*? _____
   What's the last sound in *egg*? _____
   How many syllables are in the word *egg*? _____
   How many sounds are in the word *egg*? _____

4. **ice cream**

   What's the first sound in *ice*? _____
   What's the last sound in *ice*? _____
   What's the first sound in *cream*? _____
   What's the last sound in *cream*? _____
   How many syllables are in the words *ice cream*? _____
   How many sounds are in the words *ice cream*? _____

5. **cheese**

   What's the first sound in *cheese*? _____
   What's the last sound in *cheese*? _____
   How many syllables are in the word *cheese*? _____
   How many sounds are in the word *cheese*? _____

6. **potato**

   What's the first sound in *potato*? _____
   What's the last sound in *potato*? _____
   How many syllables are in the word *potato*? _____
   How many sounds are in the word *potato*? _____

125

7. **sandwich**

   What's the first sound in *sandwich*? _____

   What's the last sound in *sandwich*? _____

   How many syllables are in the word *sandwich*? _____

   How many sounds are in the word *sandwich*? _____

8. **bread**

   What's the first sound in *bread*? _____

   What's the last sound in *bread*? _____

   How many syllables are in the word *bread*? _____

   How many sounds are in the word *bread*? _____

9. **butter**

   What's the first sound in *butter*? _____

   What's the last sound in *butter*? _____

   How many syllables are in the word *butter*? _____

   How many sounds are in the word *butter*? _____

10. **apple**

    What's the first sound in *apple*? _____

    What's the last sound in *apple*? _____

    How many syllables are in the word *apple*? _____

    How many sounds are in the word *apple*? _____

11. **grapes**

    What's the first sound in *grapes*? _____

    What's the last sound in *grapes*? _____

    How many syllables are in the word *grapes*? _____

    How many sounds are in the word *grapes*? _____

12. **orange**

    What's the first sound in *orange*? _____

    What's the last sound in *orange*? _____

    How many syllables are in the word *orange*? _____

    How many sounds are in the word *orange*? _____

13. **cherries**

    What's the first sound in *cherries*? _____

    What's the last sound in *cherries*? _____

    How many syllables are in the word *cherries*? _____

    How many sounds are in the word *cherries*? _____

14. **banana**

What's the first sound in *banana*?   _____

What's the last sound in *banana*?   _____

How many syllables are in the word *banana*?   _____

How many sounds are in the word *banana*?   _____

15. **lemon**

What's the first sound in *lemon*?   _____

What's the last sound in *lemon*?   _____

How many syllables are in the word *lemon*?   _____

How many sounds are in the word *lemon*?   _____

16. **lettuce**

What's the first sound in *lettuce*?   _____

What's the last sound in *lettuce*?   _____

How many syllables are in the word *lettuce*?   _____

How many sounds are in the word *lettuce*?   _____

17. **tomato**

What's the first sound in *tomato*?   _____

What's the last sound in *tomato*?   _____

How many syllables are in the word *tomato*?   _____

How many sounds are in the word *tomato*?   _____

18. **corn**

What's the first sound in *corn*?   _____

What's the last sound in *corn*?   _____

How many syllables are in the word *corn*?   _____

How many sounds are in the word *corn*?   _____

19. **carrot**

What's the first sound in *carrot*?   _____

What's the last sound in *carrot*?   _____

How many syllables are in the word *carrot*?   _____

How many sounds are in the word *carrot*?   _____

20. **French fries**

What's the first sound in *French*?   _____

What's the last sound in *French*?   _____

What's the first sound in *fries*?   _____

What's the last sound in *fries*?   _____

How many syllables are in the words *French fries*?   _____

How many sounds are in the words *French fries*?   _____

Vocabulary Objectives

Annual Goal

Student will demonstrate increased receptive and expressive vocabulary skills.

Short-Term Objectives/Benchmarks

Objective *1*

When the clinician verbally gives self-care item target vocabulary words, the student will point to pictures of these items with 80% accuracy.

Clinician:	Guadalupe, point to *shoes*. Point to *hat*.
Student:	(Points to each named picture.)

Objective *2*

When the clinician holds up a picture and says, "Is this a(n) _____?" the student will verbally or nonverbally indicate *yes* or *no* with 80% accuracy.

Clinician:	(Holds up a picture of a *dress*.) Mario, is this a *hat*?
Student:	No. (Says verbally or shakes head *no.*)

Clinician:	(Holds up a picture of *socks*.) Pedro, are these *socks*?
Student:	Yes. (Says verbally or shakes head *yes.*)

Objective *3*

When the clinician gives a 1-2 sentence verbal description of a target word/concept and gives the student two choices of answers, the student will verbally supply the correct answer with 80% accuracy.

Clinician:	Listen, Petunia. These are things we wear on our feet. We put these on before we put shoes on. Are they *socks* or *pants*?
Student:	Socks.

Objective *4*

When shown pictures of self-care item target vocabulary words, the student will give verbal, one-word labels with 80% accuracy.

Clinician:	(Shows picture of a *tie*.) Talia, what's this?
Student:	Tie.

129

Objective 5

When asked to verbally list 3-5 items in a given category, the student will do so with 80% accuracy.

Clinician: Hannah, tell me the names of four different kinds of clothes we wear.
Student: Hat, shoes, coat, pants.

Objective 6

When asked to define a self-care item target vocabulary word, the student will give a 5+ word verbal description with 80% accuracy.

Clinician: Tran, what is a *dress*?
Student: It is something a lady wears.

Objective 7

When given a self-care item target vocabulary word, the student will use the word in a sentence with 80% accuracy.

Clinician: Vien, please use the word *glasses* in a sentence.
Student: People wear glasses so they can see better.

For more advanced students: (written language)

Objective 8

When presented with a paragraph or word list containing the self-care item target vocabulary word, the student will find and read the word out loud with 80% accuracy.

Clinician: Finn, look at this story. Please find the word *scarf*, and read the word to me after you find it.
Student: (Reads story.) Scarf. (Reads word aloud.)

Objective 9

When asked to spell a target vocabulary word, the student will spell the word out loud with 80% accuracy.

Clinician: Rebecca, please spell the word *pants*.
Student: (Spells the word out loud.)

Objective 10

When given a target vocabulary word, the student will write a sentence containing the word with 80% accuracy.

Clinician: Lindy, please write the word *boots* in a sentence.
Student: (Writes a sentence containing the word *boots*.)

Phonological Awareness Objectives

Annual Goal
Student will demonstrate increased phonological awareness skills.

Short-Term Objectives/Benchmarks

Objective 11 With 80% accuracy, the student will count the number of words in a sentence that is prewritten or that the student has written.

> *Clinician:* Look, Carlotta. Here is a sentence in our story. Count how many words are in that sentence.
> *Student:* (Counts the number of words in the sentence.)

> *Clinician:* Paulina, you wrote a good sentence using the word *glasses*. Please count how many words are in your sentence.
> *Student:* (Counts the number of words in the sentence.)

Objective 12 When given a target vocabulary word, the student will identify the number of syllables in that word with 80% accuracy.

> *Clinician:* Nina, how many syllables are in the word *brush*?
> *Student:* One.

Objective 13 When given a target vocabulary word, the student will identify the number of sounds in that word with 80% accuracy.

> *Clinician:* Emilio, how many sounds are in the word *boots*?
> *Student:* Four.

Objective 14 When the student hears a word that rhymes with a target vocabulary word, the student will identify that word verbally or nonverbally with 80% accuracy.

> *Clinician:* Karinna, color the picture that rhymes with *sigh*.
> *Student:* (Colors the picture of the tie.)

> *Clinician:* Omar, what item of clothing rhymes with *sat*?
> *Student:* Hat.

131

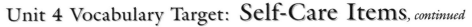

Objective 15 When the student hears the speech pathologist say a target vocabulary word phoneme by phoneme, that student will demonstrate sound blending skills by stating the whole word with 80% accuracy.

Clinician: Montero, what word is this? /d/-/r/-/e/-/ss/
Student: Dress.

Objective 16 When given a target vocabulary word, the student will identify the first sound in that word upon request with 80% accuracy.

Clinician: Listen, Michaela. *Toothbrush*. What's the first sound in that word?
Student: /t/

Objective 17 When given a target vocabulary word, the student will identify the last sound in that word upon request with 80% accuracy.

Clinician: Listen, Viktor. *Comb*. What's the last sound in that word?
Student: /m/

Unit 4: Self-Care Items

Target Words	Objective 1		Objective 2		Objective 3		Objective 4		Objective 5		Objective 6	
Unit 4: Self-Care Items	point to pictures		yes/no		2-choice answer		1-word label		list items		verbal definition	
+ Correct − Incorrect	Pretest Date	Posttest Date	Pretest Date	Posttest Date	Pretest Date	Posttest Date	Pretest Date	Posttest Date	Pretest Date	Posttest Date	Pretest Date	Posttest Date
1. belt												
2. boots												
3. brush												
4. coat												
5. comb												
6. dress												
7. glasses												
8. hat												
9. pants												
10. scarf												
11. shirt												
12. shoes												
13. shorts												
14. skirt												
15. soap												
16. socks												
17. tie												
18. toothbrush												
19. toothpaste												
20. towel												
	% Correct	% Correct	% Correct	% Correct	% Correct	% Correct	% Correct	% Correct	% Correct	% Correct	% Correct	% Correct

Unit 4: Self-Care Items

Target Words	Objective 7. say word in sentence		Objective 8 read word in paragraph		Objective 9 spell the word		Objective 10 write word in sentence		Objective 11 count words in sentence		Objective 12 count syllables in word	
Unit 4: Self-Care Items	Pretest Date	Posttest Date	Pretest Date	Posttest Date	Pretest Date	Posttest Date	Pretest Date	Posttest Date	Pretest Date	Posttest Date	Pretest Date	Posttest Date
+ Correct – Incorrect												
1. belt												
2. boots												
3. brush												
4. coat												
5. comb												
6. dress												
7. glasses												
8. hat												
9. pants												
10. scarf												
11. shirt												
12. shoes												
13. shorts												
14. skirt												
15. soap												
16. socks												
17. tie												
18. toothbrush												
19. toothpaste												
20. towel												
	% Correct	% Correct	% Correct	% Correct	% Correct	% Correct	% Correct	% Correct	% Correct	% Correct	% Correct	% Correct

Unit 4: Self-Care Items

Target Words	Objective 13		Objective 14		Objective 15		Objective 16		Objective 17	
Unit 4: Self-Care Items	identify number of sounds in word		identify rhyming word		sound blending		identify first sound in word		identify last sound in word	
+ Correct – Incorrect	Pretest Date	Posttest Date	Pretest Date	Posttest Date	Pretest Date	Posttest Date	Pretest Date	Posttest Date	Pretest Date	Posttest Date
1. belt										
2. boots										
3. brush										
4. coat										
5. comb										
6. dress										
7. glasses										
8. hat										
9. pants										
10. scarf										
11. shirt										
12. shoes										
13. shorts										
14. skirt										
15. soap										
16. socks										
17. tie										
18. toothbrush										
19. toothpaste										
20. towel										
	% Correct	% Correct	% Correct	% Correct	% Correct	% Correct	% Correct	% Correct	% Correct	% Correct

Vocabulary Pictures: Cut pictures apart to use in the activities that follow.

Vocabulary Pictures: Cut pictures apart to use in the activities that follow.

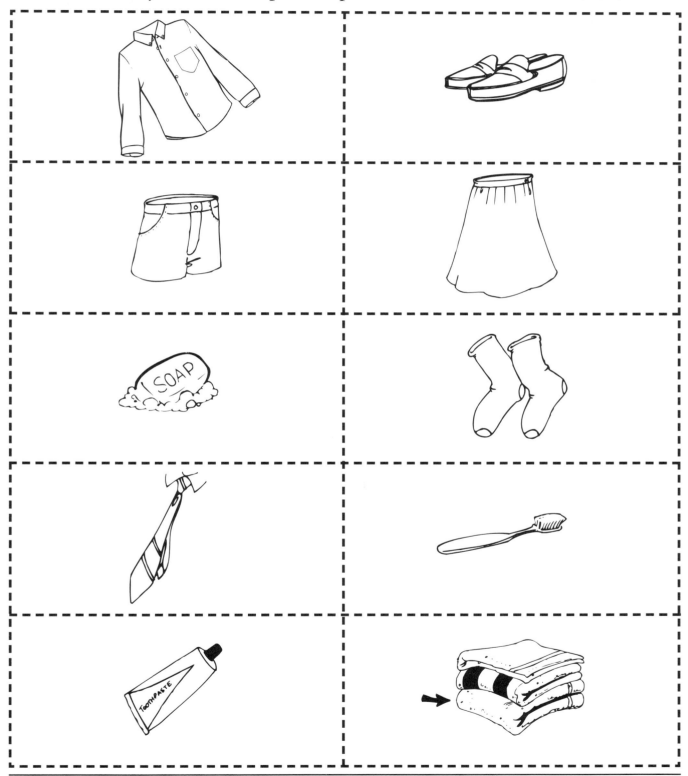

There are many uses for these Word Cards, including having your students pair them with the picture cards, reading the words aloud (if students are able), or copying the words on the lines for practice. Use these vocabulary words in any way you see fit.

belt	boots	brush
____	____	____
coat	comb	dress
____	____	____
glasses	hat	pants
____	____	____
scarf	shirt	shoes
____	____	____
shorts	skirt	soap
____	____	____
socks	tie	toothbrush
____	____	____
toothpaste	towel	
____	____	

Vocabulary Word Definitions

belt A strip of material worn around the waist. It usually has a buckle and helps hold up pants.

boots These are worn on the feet, often during cold or rainy weather. They cover part of a person's legs.

brush A thing with a handle and bristles on the end. We run the bristles through our hair to make it neat.

coat This is worn over our clothes. It usually opens in the front and has sleeves. We use it to keep us warm.

comb A thin piece of rubber, plastic, or metal. It has teeth that we run through our hair to make it neat.

dress A piece of clothing a girl or woman wears. It is all one piece with a skirt on the bottom.

glasses Things people wear near their eyes to help them see better.

hat A cover for the head. Sometimes it has a brim.

pants A piece of clothing that goes from the waist to the feet. They are divided in two, and one leg goes into each side.

scarf A piece of clothing worn around the neck and head to keep us warm.

shirt Clothing worn on the top of the body. It usually has short or long sleeves.

shoes Coverings we wear on our feet to keep our feet safe. They usually have soles on the bottom.

shorts A piece of clothing that starts at the waist and ends above the knee. We usually wear them in the summer.

skirt A piece of clothing that girls and women wear. It goes on the lower part of the body and hangs down from the waist.

soap An item that usually comes in a bar. We use it to wash ourselves.

socks Soft, short stockings that come only partway to the knee. We usually wear them with shoes.

tie A skinny piece of cloth that people wear around the neck.

toothbrush A long and skinny brush that has soft bristles at the end. We use it to brush and clean our teeth.

toothpaste A minty paste that comes in a tube. We put it on a toothbrush to help clean our teeth.

towel A large cloth we use to dry our skin after we get it wet.

Activity 1: Self-Care Items

Have your students complete each definition with a word from the box. (Do this orally with nonreading students.)

comb	soap	shoes	tie	glasses
brush	toothbrush	shirt	boots	shorts

1. _____ are a piece of clothing that starts at the waist and ends above the knee. We usually wear them in the summer.

2. _____ are things people wear near their eyes to help them see better.

3. A _____ is a thin piece of rubber, plastic, or metal. It has teeth that we run through our hair to make it neat.

4. _____ are coverings we wear on our feet to keep our feet safe. They usually have soles on the bottom.

5. A _____ is a skinny piece of cloth that people wear around the neck.

6. A _____ is clothing worn on the top of the body. It usually has short or long sleeves.

7. A _____ is a long and skinny brush that has soft bristles at the end. We use it to brush and clean our teeth.

8. _____ are worn on the feet, often during cold or rainy weather. They cover part of a person's legs.

9. A _____ is a thing with a handle and bristles on the end. We run the bristles through our hair to make it neat.

10. _____ usually comes in a bar. We use it to wash ourselves.

| toothpaste | socks | dress | hat | scarf |
| towel | pants | skirt | coat | belt |

11. A _____ is a strip of material worn around the waist. It usually has a buckle and helps hold up pants.

12. _____ are soft, short stockings that come only partway to the knee. We usually wear them with shoes.

13. A _____ is a piece of clothing worn around the neck and head to keep us warm.

14. _____ is a minty paste that comes in a tube. We put it on a toothbrush to help clean our teeth.

15. A _____ is a piece of clothing that girls and women wear. It goes on the lower part of the body and hangs down from the waist.

16. A _____ is a large cloth we use to dry our skin after we get it wet.

17. _____ are a piece of clothing that goes from the waist to the feet. They are divided in two, and one leg goes into each side.

18. A _____ is worn over our clothes. It usually opens in the front and has sleeves. We use it to keep us warm.

19. A _____ is a piece of clothing a girl or a woman wears. It is all one piece with a skirt on the bottom.

20. A _____ is a cover for the head. Sometimes it has a brim.

Activity 2: Self-Care Items

Holding up a picture of each item, have your students verbally supply the correct answer. (If students are advanced enough to read, they may circle the correct answers on their own.)

1. These are a piece of clothing that goes from the waist to the feet. They are divided in two, and one leg goes into each side.

    What are they?   **boots**   **pants**

2. This is a piece of clothing a girl or woman wears. It is all one piece with a skirt on the bottom.

    What is it?   **dress**   **comb**

3. This is a cover for the head. Sometimes it has a brim.

    What is it?   **hat**   **tie**

4. These are soft, short stockings that come only partway to the knee. We usually wear them with shoes.

    What are they?   **glasses**   **socks**

5. This is long and skinny and has soft bristles at the end. We use it to brush and clean our teeth.

    What is it?   **toothbrush**   **belt**

6. These are things people wear near their eyes to help them see better.

    What are they?   **shoes**   **glasses**

7. These are worn on the feet, often during cold or rainy weather. They cover part of a person's legs.

    What are they?   **shorts**   **boots**

8. This is a piece of clothing worn around the neck and head to help keep us warm.

    What is it?   **scarf**   **dress**

9. This is a piece of clothing that girls and women wear. It goes on the lower part of the body and hangs down from the waist.

    What is it?   **towel**   **skirt**

10. This is a thin piece of rubber, plastic, or metal. It has teeth that we run through our hair to make it neat.

    What is it?   **comb**   **scarf**

11. These are a piece of clothing that starts at the waist and ends above the knee. We usually wear them in the summer.

    What are they?   **glasses**   **shorts**

12. This is a thing with a handle and bristles on the end. We run the bristles through our hair to make it neat.

    What is it?   **brush**   **soap**

13. This is worn over our clothes. It usually opens in the front and has sleeves. We use it to keep warm.

    What is it?   **skirt**   **coat**

14. This is a minty paste that comes in a tube. We put it on a toothbrush to help clean our teeth.

    What is it?   **toothpaste**   **soap**

15. This is worn on the top of the body. It usually has short or long sleeves.

    What is it?   **belt**   **shirt**

16. These are coverings we wear on our feet to keep our feet safe. They usually have soles on the bottom.

    What are they?   **shorts**   **shoes**

17. This is a large cloth we use to dry our skin after we get it wet.

    What is it?   **towel**   **skirt**

18. This is a strip of material worn around the waist. It usually has a buckle and helps hold up pants.

    What is it?   **belt**   **hat**

19. This usually comes in a bar. We use it to wash ourselves.

    What is it?   **shirt**   **soap**

20. This is a skinny piece of cloth that people wear around the neck.

    What is it?   **comb**   **tie**

Activity 3: Self-Care Items

Have your student read the story. Ask him to find each vocabulary word and circle it as he reads. Your student can use the word cards on page 138 as a reference. The story contains all 20 vocabulary words.

The Vang family was going shopping to buy things for their vacation. They were going to travel to a beautiful place where there were not very many stores, so they had to buy a lot of things. They bought each family member a toothbrush, and they bought a tube of toothpaste for the whole family. They decided to also buy everybody a comb and brush for their hair. The Vangs bought two bars of soap and several towels just in case they needed them. It wasn't cold or rainy where they were going, so they decided that no one needed a coat, scarf, or boots. In case they went someplace nice, Dad decided that he should bring a tie. Mom and the girls each brought a dress and a skirt.

The Vangs were going to be doing a lot of fun things outside during their vacation. As they packed, they made sure that they all had several pairs of socks and some comfortable shoes. Each person also brought a hat to protect himself from the hot sun. They realized that they would each need to bring shirts, shorts, pants, and one belt each. As they were leaving, Mom said to Dad, "Remember to bring your glasses!" The Vang family was well prepared for vacation!

Optional Activities:

- ◆ Ask students to retell the story.
- ◆ Read the story out loud. Afterwards, ask questions about the story and have students provide answers. For example, "Why was the Vang family going shopping? What did they need to buy?"
- ◆ After reading the story out loud, pick target vocabulary words out of the story and say each word phoneme by phoneme to allow students to practice sound blending. Example: "/H/-/a/-/t/; what word is that?" (Objective 15)
- ◆ Pick out a sentence and ask a student to count the number of words in the sentence. (Objective 11)
- ◆ Have students read the story silently or out loud to practice reading skills.
- ◆ After students are familiar with the story, read it out loud and omit the target vocabulary words. Have the students orally fill in the blanks.

Activity 4: Self-Care Items

Have your students complete these items to fulfill the listed objectives. Nonreading and nonwriting students can dictate the sentence while you transcribe it. (Objective 7)

1. Use the word *comb* in a sentence.

   _____

   _____

   How many words are in your sentence? _____

   How many syllables are in the word *comb*? _____

   How many sounds are in the word *comb*? _____

2. Use the word *glasses* in a sentence.

   _____

   _____

   How many words are in your sentence? _____

   How many syllables are in the word *glasses*? _____

   How many sounds are in the word *glasses*? _____

3. Use the word *tie* in a sentence.

   _____

   _____

   How many words are in your sentence? _____

   How many syllables are in the word *tie*? _____

   How many sounds are in the word *tie*? _____

4. Use the word *coat* in a sentence.

   _____

   _____

   How many words are in your sentence? _____

   How many syllables are in the word *coat*? _____

   How many sounds are in the word *coat*? _____

5. Use the word *toothpaste* in a sentence.

   _____

   _____

   How many words are in your sentence? _____

   How many syllables are in the word *toothpaste*? _____

   How many sounds are in the word *toothpaste*? _____

6. Use the word *boots* in a sentence.

_____

_____

      How many words are in your sentence?   _____

      How many syllables are in the word *boots*?   _____

      How many sounds are in the word *boots*?   _____

7. Use the word *dress* in a sentence.

_____

_____

      How many words are in your sentence?   _____

      How many syllables are in the word *dress*?   _____

      How many sounds are in the word *dress*?   _____

8. Use the word *brush* in a sentence.

_____

_____

      How many words are in your sentence?   _____

      How many syllables are in the word *brush*?   _____

      How many sounds are in the word *brush*?   _____

9. Use the word *skirt* in a sentence.

_____

_____

      How many words are in your sentence?   _____

      How many syllables are in the word *skirt*?   _____

      How many sounds are in the word *skirt*?   _____

10. Use the word *pants* in a sentence.

_____

_____

      How many words are in your sentence?   _____

      How many syllables are in the word *pants*?   _____

      How many sounds are in the word *pants*?   _____

11. Use the word *towel* in a sentence.

_____

_____

      How many words are in your sentence?   _____

      How many syllables are in the word *towel*?   _____

      How many sounds are in the word *towel*?   _____

12. Use the word *hat* in a sentence.

_____

_____

      How many words are in your sentence?   _____

      How many syllables are in the word *hat*?   _____

      How many sounds are in the word *hat*?   _____

13. Use the word *toothbrush* in a sentence.

_____

_____

      How many words are in your sentence?   _____

      How many syllables are in the word *toothbrush*? _____

      How many sounds are in the word *toothbrush*? _____

14. Use the word *belt* in a sentence.

_____

_____

      How many words are in your sentence?   _____

      How many syllables are in the word *belt*?   _____

      How many sounds are in the word *belt*?   _____

15. Use the word *soap* in a sentence.

_____

_____

      How many words are in your sentence?   _____

      How many syllables are in the word *soap*?   _____

      How many sounds are in the word *soap*?   _____

16. Use the word *shirt* in a sentence.

_____

_____

      How many words are in your sentence?   _____

      How many syllables are in the word *shirt*?   _____

      How many sounds are in the word *shirt*?   _____

17. Use the word *shorts* in a sentence.

_____

_____

      How many words are in your sentence?   _____

      How many syllables are in the word *shorts*?   _____

      How many sounds are in the word *shorts*?   _____

18. Use the word *shoes* in a sentence.

_____

_____

      How many words are in your sentence?   _____

      How many syllables are in the word *shoes*?   _____

      How many sounds are in the word *shoes*?   _____

19. Use the word *scarf* in a sentence.

_____

_____

      How many words are in your sentence?   _____

      How many syllables are in the word *scarf*?   _____

      How many sounds are in the word *scarf*?   _____

20. Use the word *socks* in a sentence.

_____

_____

      How many words are in your sentence?   _____

      How many syllables are in the word *socks*?   _____

      How many sounds are in the word *socks*?   _____

Activity 5: Self-Care Items

Have your students complete these items to fulfill the listed objective. Tell the students that some of these are silly, made-up words.

1. Circle the one that rhymes with *melt*.

2. Circle the one that rhymes with *darf*.

3. Circle the one that rhymes with *courts*.

4. Circle the one that rhymes with *tasses*.

5. Circle the one that rhymes with *boat*.

6. Circle the one that rhymes with *fruits*.

7. Circle the one that rhymes with *sat*.

8. Circle the one that rhymes with *lie.*

9. Circle the one that rhymes with *dirt*.

10. Circle the one that rhymes with *less*.

11. Circle the one that rhymes with *ants*.

12. Circle the one that rhymes with *squirt*.

13. Circle the one that rhymes with *locks*.

14. Circle the one that rhymes with *lose*.

15. Circle the one that rhymes with *foul*.

16. Circle the one that rhymes with *koothpaste*.

17. Circle the one that rhymes with *zoothbrush*.

18. Circle the one that rhymes with *rope*.

19. Circle the one that rhymes with *mush*.

20. Circle the one that rhymes with *foam*.

Activity 6: Self-Care Items

Have your students complete these items to fulfill the listed objective.

Put an X on the picture when you hear its word said sound by sound. Say the word out loud.
(Example: /b/-/e/-/l/-/t/)

Activity 7: Self-Care Items

Have your students complete these items to fulfill the listed objectives. Read each word and then ask a question. Record each student's responses in the lines provided.

1. **comb**

   What's the first sound in *comb*? _____
   What's the last sound in *comb*? _____
   How many syllables are in the word *comb*? _____
   How many sounds are in the word *comb*? _____

2. **toothbrush**

   What's the first sound in *toothbrush*? _____
   What's the last sound in *toothbrush*? _____
   How many syllables are in the word *toothbrush*? _____
   How many sounds are in the word *toothbrush*? _____

3. **shoes**

   What's the first sound in *shoes*? _____
   What's the last sound in *shoes*? _____
   How many syllables are in the word *shoes*? _____
   How many sounds are in the word *shoes*? _____

4. **dress**

   What's the first sound in *dress*? _____
   What's the last sound in *dress*? _____
   How many syllables are in the word *dress*? _____
   How many sounds are in the word *dress*? _____

5. **tie**

   What's the first sound in *tie*? _____
   What's the last sound in *tie*? _____
   How many syllables are in the word *tie*? _____
   How many sounds are in the word *tie*? _____

6. **coat**

   What's the first sound in *coat*? _____
   What's the last sound in *coat*? _____
   How many syllables are in the word *coat*? _____
   How many sounds are in the word *coat*? _____

7. **scarf**

What's the first sound in *scarf*? _____
What's the last sound in *scarf*? _____
How many syllables are in the word *scarf*? _____
How many sounds are in the word *scarf*? _____

8. **brush**

What's the first sound in *brush*? _____
What's the last sound in *brush*? _____
How many syllables are in the word *brush*? _____
How many sounds are in the word *brush*? _____

9. **toothpaste**

What's the first sound in *toothpaste*? _____
What's the last sound in *toothpaste*? _____
How many syllables are in the word *toothpaste*? _____
How many sounds are in the word *toothpaste*? _____

10. **socks**

What's the first sound in *socks*? _____
What's the last sound in *socks*? _____
How many syllables are in the word *socks*? _____
How many sounds are in the word *socks*? _____

11. **shirt**

What's the first sound in *shirt*? _____
What's the last sound in *shirt*? _____
How many syllables are in the word *shirt*? _____
How many sounds are in the word *shirt*? _____

12. **hat**

What's the first sound in *hat*? _____
What's the last sound in *hat*? _____
How many syllables are in the word *hat*? _____
How many sounds are in the word *hat*? _____

13. **glasses**

What's the first sound in *glasses*? _____
What's the last sound in *glasses*? _____
How many syllables are in the word *glasses*? _____
How many sounds are in the word *glasses*? _____

14. **belt**

What's the first sound in *belt*? ____
What's the last sound in *belt*? ____
How many syllables are in the word *belt*? ____
How many sounds are in the word *belt*? ____

15. **soap**

What's the first sound in *soap*? ____
What's the last sound in *soap*? ____
How many syllables are in the word *soap*? ____
How many sounds are in the word *soap*? ____

16. **towel**

What's the first sound in *towel*? ____
What's the last sound in *towel*? ____
How many syllables are in the word *towel*? ____
How many sounds are in the word *towel*? ____

17. **pants**

What's the first sound in *pants*? ____
What's the last sound in *pants*? ____
How many syllables are in the word *pants*? ____
How many sounds are in the word *pants*? ____

18. **skirt**

What's the first sound in *skirt*? ____
What's the last sound in *skirt*? ____
How many syllables are in the word *skirt*? ____
How many sounds are in the word *skirt*? ____

19. **boots**

What's the first sound in *boots*? ____
What's the last sound in *boots*? ____
How many syllables are in the word *boots*? ____
How many sounds are in the word *boots*? ____

20. **shorts**

What's the first sound in *shorts*? ____
What's the last sound in *shorts*? ____
How many syllables are in the words *shorts*? ____
How many sounds are in the words *shorts*? ____

Vocabulary Objectives

Annual Goal

Student will demonstrate increased receptive and expressive vocabulary skills.

Short-Term Objectives/Benchmarks

Objective 1

When the clinician verbally gives animal target vocabulary words, the student will point to pictures of these items with 80% accuracy.

Clinician: George, point to *cat*. Point to *dog*.
Student: (Points to each named picture.)

Objective 2

When the clinician holds up a picture and says, "Is this a(n) _____?" the student will verbally or nonverbally indicate *yes* or *no* with 80% accuracy.

Clinician: (Holds up a picture of a *horse*.) Trang, is this a *chicken*?
Student: No. (Says verbally or shakes head *no.*)

Clinician: (Holds up a picture of a *cow*.) Danica, is this a *cow*?
Student: Yes. (Says verbally or shakes head *yes.*)

Objective 3

When the clinician gives a 1-2 sentence verbal description of a target word/concept and gives the student two choices of answers, the student will verbally supply the correct answer with 80% accuracy.

Clinician: Listen, Tina. This is furry and meows and purrs. Is it a *horse* or a *cat*?
Student: Cat.

Objective 4

When shown pictures of animal item target vocabulary words, the student will give verbal, one-word labels with 80% accuracy.

Clinician: (Shows picture of a *fish*.) Martin, what's this?
Student: Fish.

Objective 5

When asked to verbally list 3-5 items in a given category, the student will do so with 80% accuracy.

Clinician: Lynn, tell me the names of four different animals.
Student: Dog, cat, fish, bird.

Objective 6

When asked to define a target vocabulary word, the student will give a 5+ word verbal description with 80% accuracy.

Clinician: Thomas, what is a *fish*?
Student: It swims in the water and has scales.

Objective 7

When given an animal target vocabulary word, the student will use the word in a sentence with 80% accuracy.

Clinician: Fong, please use the word *dog* in a sentence.
Student: A dog is an animal that has fur and barks.

For more advanced students: (written language)

Objective 8

When presented with a paragraph or word list containing the animal target vocabulary word, the student will find and read the word out loud with 80% accuracy.

Clinician: Andre, look at this story. Please find the word *horse*, and read the word to me after you find it.
Student: (Reads story.) Horse. (Reads word aloud.)

Objective 9

When asked to spell a target vocabulary word, the student will spell the word out loud with 80% accuracy.

Clinician: Stefani, please spell the word *elephant*.
Student: (Spells the word out loud.)

Objective 10

When given a target vocabulary word, the student will write a sentence containing the word.

Clinician: Esther, please write the word *pig* in a sentence.
Student: (Writes a sentence containing the word *pig*.)

Phonological Awareness Objectives

Annual Goal Student will demonstrate increased phonological awareness skills.

Short-Term Objectives/Benchmarks

Objective 11 With 80% accuracy, the student will count the number of words in a sentence that is prewritten or that the student has written.

Clinician: Look, Leticia. Here is a sentence in our story. Count how many words are in that sentence.
Student: (Counts the number of words in the sentence.)

Clinician: Kaysha, you wrote a good sentence using the word *tiger*. Please count how many words are in your sentence.
Student: (Counts the number of words in the sentence.)

Objective 12 When given a target vocabulary word, the student will identify the number of syllables in that word with 80% accuracy.

Clinician: Hanua, how many syllables are in the word *elephant*?
Student: Three.

Objective 13 When given a target vocabulary word, the student will identify the number of sounds in that word with 80% accuracy.

Clinician: Permeika, how many sounds are in the word *fish*?
Student: Three.

Objective 14 When the student hears a word that rhymes with a target vocabulary word, the student will identify that word verbally or nonverbally with 80% accuracy.

Clinician: Katja, color the picture that rhymes with *log*.
Student: (Colors the picture of the dog.)

Clinician: Justine, what animal rhymes with *course*?
Student: Horse.

159

Objective 15

When the student hears the speech pathologist say a target vocabulary word phoneme by phoneme, that student will demonstrate sound blending skills by stating the whole word with 80% accuracy.

Clinician: Tony, what word is this? /b/-/ir/-/d/
Student: Bird.

Objective 16

When given a target vocabulary word, the student will identify the first sound in that word upon request with 80% accuracy.

Clinician: Listen, Michael. *Pig.* What's the first sound in that word?
Student: /p/

Objective 17

When given a target vocabulary word, the student will identify the last sound in that word upon request with 80% accuracy.

Clinician: Listen, Chloe. *Horse.* What's the last sound in that word?
Student: /s/

Target Words	Objective 1		Objective 2		Objective 3		Objective 4		Objective 5		Objective 6	
Unit 5: Animals	point to pictures		yes/no		2-choice answer		1-word label		list items		verbal definition	
+ Correct − Incorrect	Pretest Date	Posttest Date	Pretest Date	Posttest Date	Pretest Date	Posttest Date	Pretest Date	Posttest Date	Pretest Date	Posttest Date	Pretest Date	Posttest Date
1. bear												
2. bird												
3. cat												
4. chicken												
5. cow												
6. dog												
7. duck												
8. elephant												
9. fish												
10. horse												
11. lion												
12. monkey												
13. mouse												
14. pig												
15. rabbit												
16. sheep												
17. snake												
18. spider												
19. tiger												
20. zebra												
	% Correct	% Correct	% Correct	% Correct	% Correct	% Correct	% Correct	% Correct	% Correct	% Correct	% Correct	% Correct

Unit 5: Animals

Target Words Unit 5: Animals	Objective 7 say word in sentence		Objective 8 read word in paragraph		Objective 9 spell the word		Objective 10 write word in sentence		Objective 11 count words in sentence		Objective 12 count syllables in word	
+ Correct – Incorrect	Pretest Date	Posttest Date	Pretest Date	Posttest Date	Pretest Date	Posttest Date	Pretest Date	Posttest Date	Pretest Date	Posttest Date	Pretest Date	Posttest Date
1. bear												
2. bird												
3. cat												
4. chicken												
5. cow												
6. dog												
7. duck												
8. elephant												
9. fish												
10. horse												
11. lion												
12. monkey												
13. mouse												
14. pig												
15. rabbit												
16. sheep												
17. snake												
18. spider												
19. tiger												
20. zebra												
	% Correct	% Correct	% Correct	% Correct	% Correct	% Correct	% Correct	% Correct	% Correct	% Correct	% Correct	% Correct

Unit 5: Animals

Target Words	Objective 13 identify number of sounds in word		Objective 14 identify rhyming word		Objective 15 sound blending		Objective 16 identify first sound in word		Objective 17 identify last sound in word	
Unit 5: Animals	Pretest Date	Posttest Date	Pretest Date	Posttest Date	Pretest Date	Posttest Date	Pretest Date	Posttest Date	Pretest Date	Posttest Date
+ Correct − Incorrect										
1. bear										
2. bird										
3. cat										
4. chicken										
5. cow										
6. dog										
7. duck										
8. elephant										
9. fish										
10. horse										
11. lion										
12. monkey										
13. mouse										
14. pig										
15. rabbit										
16. sheep										
17. snake										
18. spider										
19. tiger										
20. zebra										
% Correct	% Correct	% Correct	% Correct	% Correct	% Correct	% Correct	% Correct	% Correct	% Correct	% Correct

Vocabulary Pictures: Cut these pictures apart to use in the activities that follow.

Vocabulary Pictures: Cut these pictures apart to use in the activities that follow.

There are many uses for these Word Cards, including having your students pair them with the picture cards, reading the words aloud (if students are able), or copying the words on the lines for practice. Use these vocabulary words in any way you see fit.

bear	bird	cat
chicken	cow	dog
duck	elephant	fish
horse	lion	monkey
mouse	pig	rabbit
sheep	snake	spider
tiger	zebra	

Vocabulary Word Definitions

bear	A big animal with shaggy fur and a very short tail. It likes to eat honey.
bird	An animal with feathers and wings. It flies in the air.
cat	An animal with fur and whiskers. It meows and purrs.
chicken	An animal with two legs, wings, and feathers. It lays eggs and says, "Cluck, cluck."
cow	A big animal that gives milk. It says, "Moo."
dog	An animal with fur and whiskers. It barks and wags its tail.
duck	An animal that has two legs and feathers. It can walk and swim. It says, "Quack, quack."
elephant	A very big animal that is usually gray. It has big ears and a long trunk.
fish	An animal that swims and lives in the water. It has scales and fins on its body.
horse	A big animal with a mane and a tail. People can ride it. It says, "Neigh."
lion	A big animal with fur and a mane. It can roar loudly.
monkey	An animal that has fur and a long tail. It likes to climb trees and eat bananas.
mouse	A small animal that has little ears and a long skinny tail. It likes to eat cheese.
pig	An animal that has a snout, hooves, and a curly tail. It says, "Oink, oink."
rabbit	An animal that is covered with fur. It hops and sometimes eats carrots.
sheep	An animal that is covered with wool. It says, "Baa."
snake	A reptile that has no legs. It slides along on its stomach and hisses.
spider	A bug with a round body and eight legs. It spins webs.
tiger	A big animal with fur. It has black and yellow stripes, and can roar loudly.
zebra	An animal that has black and white stripes. It looks like a horse.

Activity 1: Animals

Have your students complete each definition with a word from the box. (Do this orally with nonreading students.)

duck	cat	mouse	horse	dog
sheep	tiger	rabbit	fish	lion

1. A _____ is a small animal that has little ears and a long skinny tail. It likes to eat cheese.

2. A _____ is an animal that is covered with wool. It says, "Baa."

3. A _____ is an animal that is covered with fur. It hops and sometimes eats carrots.

4. A _____ is an animal with fur and whiskers. It meows and purrs.

5. A _____ is an animal with fur and whiskers. It barks and wags its tail.

6. A _____ is a big animal with a mane and a tail. People can ride this animal. It says, "Neigh."

7. A _____ is an animal that has two legs and feathers. It can walk and swim. It says, "Quack, quack."

8. A _____ is an animal that swims and lives in the water. It has scales and fins on its body.

9. A _____ is a big animal with fur and a mane. It can roar loudly.

10. A _____ is a big animal with fur. It has black and yellow stripes, and can roar loudly.

spider	cow	zebra	bird	snake
monkey	bear	elephant	chicken	pig

11. A _____ is an animal that has black and white stripes. It looks like a horse.

12. A _____ is a big animal that has shaggy fur and a very short tail. It likes to eat honey.

13. A _____ is an animal with feathers and wings. It flies in the air.

14. A _____ is an animal that has a snout, hooves, and a curly tail. It says, "Oink, oink."

15. A _____ is a bug with a round body and eight legs. It spins webs.

16. A _____ is a big animal that gives milk. It says, "Moo."

17. A _____ is an animal with two legs, wings, and feathers. It lays eggs and says, "Cluck, cluck."

18. An _____ is a very big animal that is usually gray. It has big ears and a long trunk.

19. A _____ is a reptile that has no legs. It slides along on its stomach and hisses.

20. A _____ is an animal that has fur and a long tail. It likes to climb trees and eat bananas.

Activity 2: Animals

Holding up a picture of each item, have your students verbally supply the correct answer. (If students are advanced enough to read, they may circle the correct answers on their own.)

1. This is a very big animal that is usually gray. It has big ears and a long trunk.

    What is it?   **duck**   **elephant**

2. This is an animal that has fur and a long tail. It likes to climb trees and eat bananas.

    What is it?   **monkey**   **pig**

3. This is a big animal with fur. It has black and yellow stripes, and can roar loudly.

    What is it?   **duck**   **tiger**

4. This is an animal that is covered with wool. It says, "Baa."

    What is it?   **sheep**   **cat**

5. This is a big animal with shaggy fur and a very short tail. It likes to eat honey.

    What is it?   **cow**   **bear**

6. This is an animal that has a snout, hooves, and a curly tail. It says, "Oink, oink."

    What is it?   **pig**   **bird**

7. This is a big animal with fur and a mane. It can roar loudly.

    What is it?   **rabbit**   **lion**

8. This is a small animal that has little ears and a long skinny tail. It likes to eat cheese.

    What is it?   **mouse**   **zebra**

9. This is a bug with a round body and eight legs. It spins webs.

    What is it?   **cow**   **spider**

10. This is an animal that has two legs and feathers. It can walk and swim. It says, "Quack, quack."

    What is it?   **monkey**   **duck**

11. This is an animal with feathers and wings. It flies in the air.

    What is it?   **fish**   **bird**

12. This is an animal with fur and whiskers. It meows and purrs.

    What is it?   **cat**   **sheep**

13. This is a big animal with a mane and a tail. People can ride this animal. It says, "Neigh."

    What is it?   **horse**   **spider**

14. This is an animal with two legs, wings, and feathers. It lays eggs and says, "Cluck, cluck."

    What is it?   **elephant**   **chicken**

15. This is an animal that is covered with fur. It hops and sometimes eats carrots.

    What is it?   **rabbit**   **bird**

16. This is a big animal that gives milk. It says, "Moo."

    What is it?   **lion**   **cow**

17. This is an animal that has black and white stripes. It looks like a horse.

    What is it?   **pig**   **zebra**

18. This is an animal with fur and whiskers. It barks and wags its tail.

    What is it?   **dog**   **mouse**

19. This is an animal that swims and lives in the water. It has scales and fins on its body.

    What is it?   **tiger**   **fish**

20. This is a reptile that has no legs. It slides along on its stomach and hisses.

    What is it?   **sheep**   **snake**

Activity 3: Animals

Have your student read the story. Ask him to find each vocabulary word and circle it as he reads. Your student can use the word cards on page 166 as a reference. The story contains all 20 vocabulary words.

Phong was feeling happy. He and his family were on vacation. They were going to several different places. The first place they went was his grandmother's house on the farm. His grandmother had rabbits, chickens, pigs, cows, horses, ducks, and sheep.

It was fun to play with all the animals on the farm! When Phong went into the barn, he saw spiders and their spider webs. Phong's grandmother also had a dog and a cat that lived in the house. The dog and cat liked to roam all over the farm. Sometimes the cat would even catch a mouse or bird. Phong's grandmother made sure the fish were safe in their fishbowl where the cat couldn't eat them. Phong and his family had a nice time staying with his grandmother and seeing all the animals. After they were done staying with his grandmother, Phong and the family went to a big zoo.

Phong had only been to the zoo once before. He loved going back and seeing the tigers and lions roaring in their cages. Phong saw a big black bear and monkeys swinging from trees. He liked watching the zebra too. Phong decided that his favorite animal was the elephant, who was eating peanuts from the ground. But he didn't like the large snake; he thought that was scary. At the end of the trip to the zoo, Phong and his family went back home. Vacation was over. What a good time they had!

Optional Activities:

◆ Ask students to retell the story.
◆ Read the story out loud. Afterwards, ask questions about the story and have students provide answers. For example, "What did Phong's family do on their vacation? What kinds of animals did they see?"
◆ After reading the story out loud, pick target vocabulary words out of the story and say each word phoneme by phoneme to allow students to practice sound blending. Example: "/Sh/-/ee/-/p/; what word is that?" (Objective 15)
◆ Pick out a sentence and ask a student to count the number of words in the sentence. (Objective 11)
◆ Have students read the story silently or out loud to practice reading skills.
◆ After students are familiar with the story, read it out loud and omit the target vocabulary words. Have the students orally fill in the blanks.

Activity 4: Animals

Have your students complete these items to fulfill the listed objectives. Nonreading and nonwriting students can dictate the sentence while you transcribe it. (Objective 7)

1. Use the word *snake* in a sentence.

   _____

   _____

   How many words are in your sentence?   _____
   How many syllables are in the word *snake*?   _____
   How many sounds are in the word *snake*?   _____

2. Use the word *bird* in a sentence.

   _____

   _____

   How many words are in your sentence?   _____
   How many syllables are in the word *bird*?   _____
   How many sounds are in the word *bird*?   _____

3. Use the word *dog* in a sentence.

   _____

   _____

   How many words are in your sentence?   _____
   How many syllables are in the word *dog*?   _____
   How many sounds are in the word *dog*?   _____

4. Use the word *elephant* in a sentence.

   _____

   _____

   How many words are in your sentence?   _____
   How many syllables are in the word *elephant*?   _____
   How many sounds are in the word *elephant*?   _____

5. Use the word *cat* in a sentence.

   _____

   _____

   How many words are in your sentence?   _____
   How many syllables are in the word *cat*?   _____
   How many sounds are in the word *cat*?   _____

6. Use the word *monkey* in a sentence.

   _____

   _____

   How many words are in your sentence?   _____

   How many syllables are in the word *monkey*?   _____

   How many sounds are in the word *monkey*?   _____

7. Use the word *duck* in a sentence.

   _____

   _____

   How many words are in your sentence?   _____

   How many syllables are in the word *duck*?   _____

   How many sounds are in the word *duck*?   _____

8. Use the word *chicken* in a sentence.

   _____

   _____

   How many words are in your sentence?   _____

   How many syllables are in the word *chicken*?   _____

   How many sounds are in the word *chicken*?   _____

9. Use the word *cow* in a sentence.

   _____

   _____

   How many words are in your sentence?   _____

   How many syllables are in the word *cow*?   _____

   How many sounds are in the word *cow*?   _____

10. Use the word *zebra* in a sentence.

    _____

    _____

    How many words are in your sentence?   _____

    How many syllables are in the word *zebra*?   _____

    How many sounds are in the word *zebra*?   _____

11. Use the word *sheep* in a sentence.

_____

_____

How many words are in your sentence? _____
How many syllables are in the word *sheep*? _____
How many sounds are in the word *sheep*? _____

12. Use the word *tiger* in a sentence.

_____

_____

How many words are in your sentence? _____
How many syllables are in the word *tiger*? _____
How many sounds are in the word *tiger*? _____

13. Use the word *horse* in a sentence.

_____

_____

How many words are in your sentence? _____
How many syllables are in the word *horse*? _____
How many sounds are in the word *horse*? _____

14. Use the word *fish* in a sentence.

_____

_____

How many words are in your sentence? _____
How many syllables are in the word *fish*? _____
How many sounds are in the word *fish*? _____

15. Use the word *mouse* in a sentence.

_____

_____

How many words are in your sentence? _____
How many syllables are in the word *mouse*? _____
How many sounds are in the word *mouse*? _____

16. Use the word *pig* in a sentence.

_____

_____

How many words are in your sentence? _____

How many syllables are in the word *pig*? _____

How many sounds are in the word *pig*? _____

17. Use the word *rabbit* in a sentence.

_____

_____

How many words are in your sentence? _____

How many syllables are in the word *rabbit*? _____

How many sounds are in the word *rabbit*? _____

18. Use the word *bear* in a sentence.

_____

_____

How many words are in your sentence? _____

How many syllables are in the word *bear*? _____

How many sounds are in the word *bear*? _____

19. Use the word *lion* in a sentence.

_____

_____

How many words are in your sentence? _____

How many syllables are in the word *lion*? _____

How many sounds are in the word *lion*? _____

20. Use the word *spider* in a sentence.

_____

_____

How many words are in your sentence? _____

How many syllables are in the word *spider*? _____

How many sounds are in the word *spider*? _____

176

Activity 5: Animals

Have your students complete these items to fulfill the listed objective. Tell the students that some of these are silly, made-up words.

1. Circle the one that rhymes with *kabbit*.

2. Circle the one that rhymes with *course*.

3. Circle the one that rhymes with *chunky*.

4. Circle the one that rhymes with *Zion*.

5. Circle the one that rhymes with *hat*.

6. Circle the one that rhymes with *picken*.

7. Circle the one that rhymes with *luck*.

8. Circle the one that rhymes with *tebra*.

9. Circle the one that rhymes with *fake*.

10. Circle the one that rhymes with *zelephant*.

11. Circle the one that rhymes with *hog*.

12. Circle the one that rhymes with *heard*.

13. Circle the one that rhymes with *glider*.

14. Circle the one that rhymes with *hair*.

15. Circle the one that rhymes with *leap*.

16. Circle the one that rhymes with *dig*.

17. Circle the one that rhymes with *dish*.

18. Circle the one that rhymes with *how*.

19. Circle the one that rhymes with *house*.

20. Circle the one that rhymes with *figer*.

Activity 6: Animals

Have your students complete these items to fulfill the listed objective.

Put an X on the picture when you hear its word said sound by sound. Say the word out loud.
(Example: /d/-/u/-/ck/)

Activity 7: Animals

Have your students complete these items to fulfill the listed objectives. Read each word and then ask a question. Record each student's responses in the lines provided.

1. **sheep**

   What's the first sound in *sheep*?   _____
   What's the last sound in *sheep*?   _____
   How many syllables are in the word *sheep*?   _____
   How many sounds are in the word *sheep*?   _____

2. **horse**

   What's the first sound in *horse*?   _____
   What's the last sound in *horse*?   _____
   How many syllables are in the word *horse*?   _____
   How many sounds are in the word *horse*?   _____

3. **snake**

   What's the first sound in *snake*?   _____
   What's the last sound in *snake*?   _____
   How many syllables are in the word *snake*?   _____
   How many sounds are in the word *snake*?   _____

4. **cow**

   What's the first sound in *cow*?   _____
   What's the last sound in *cow*?   _____
   How many syllables are in the word *cow*?   _____
   How many sounds are in the word *cow*?   _____

5. **fish**

   What's the first sound in *fish*?   _____
   What's the last sound in *fish*?   _____
   How many syllables are in the word *fish*?   _____
   How many sounds are in the word *fish*?   _____

6. **monkey**

   What's the first sound in *monkey*?   _____
   What's the last sound in *monkey*?   _____
   How many syllables are in the word *monkey*?   _____
   How many sounds are in the word *monkey*?   _____

Activity 7: Animals, *continued*

7. **spider**

What's the first sound in *spider*? _____
What's the last sound in *spider*? _____
How many syllables are in the word *spider*? _____
How many sounds are in the word *spider*? _____

8. **dog**

What's the first sound in *dog*? _____
What's the last sound in *dog*? _____
How many syllables are in the word *dog*? _____
How many sounds are in the word *dog*? _____

9. **tiger**

What's the first sound in *tiger*? _____
What's the last sound in *tiger*? _____
How many syllables are in the word *tiger*? _____
How many sounds are in the word *tiger*? _____

10. **bear**

What's the first sound in *bear*? _____
What's the last sound in *bear*? _____
How many syllables are in the word *bear*? _____
How many sounds are in the word *bear*? _____

11. **elephant**

What's the first sound in *elephant*? _____
What's the last sound in *elephant*? _____
How many syllables are in the word *elephant*? _____
How many sounds are in the word *elephant*? _____

12. **duck**

What's the first sound in *duck*? _____
What's the last sound in *duck*? _____
How many syllables are in the word *duck*? _____
How many sounds are in the word *duck*? _____

13. **bird**

What's the first sound in *bird*? _____
What's the last sound in *bird*? _____
How many syllables are in the word *bird*? _____
How many sounds are in the word *bird*? _____

14. **cat**

What's the first sound in *cat*? _____
What's the last sound in *cat*? _____
How many syllables are in the word *cat*? _____
How many sounds are in the word *cat*? _____

15. **chicken**

What's the first sound in *chicken*? _____
What's the last sound in *chicken*? _____
How many syllables are in the word *chicken*? _____
How many sounds are in the word *chicken*? _____

16. **pig**

What's the first sound in *pig*? _____
What's the last sound in *pig*? _____
How many syllables are in the word *pig*? _____
How many sounds are in the word *pig*? _____

17. **rabbit**

What's the first sound in *rabbit*? _____
What's the last sound in *rabbit*? _____
How many syllables are in the word *rabbit*? _____
How many sounds are in the word *rabbit*? _____

18. **mouse**

What's the first sound in *mouse*? _____
What's the last sound in *mouse*? _____
How many syllables are in the word *mouse*? _____
How many sounds are in the word *mouse*? _____

19. **lion**

What's the first sound in *lion*? _____
What's the last sound in *lion*? _____
How many syllables are in the word *lion*? _____
How many sounds are in the word *lion*? _____

20. **zebra**

What's the first sound in *zebra*? _____
What's the last sound in *zebra*? _____
How many syllables are in the word *zebra*? _____
How many sounds are in the word *zebra*? _____

183

Vocabulary Objectives

> **Annual Goal**
>
> Student will demonstrate increased receptive and expressive vocabulary skills.

Short-Term Objectives/Benchmarks

Objective 1

When the clinician verbally gives time/weather/season target vocabulary words, the student will point to pictures of these items with 80% accuracy.

Clinician: Natasha, point to *calendar*. Point to *winter*.
Student: (Points to each named picture.)

Objective 2

When the clinician holds up a picture and says, "Is this a(n) _____?" the student will verbally or nonverbally indicate *yes* or *no* with 80% accuracy.

Clinician: (Holds up a picture of the *sun*.) Von, is this *snow*?
Student: No. (Says verbally or shakes head *no*.)

Clinician: (Holds up a picture of *rain*.) Soua, is this *rain*?
Student: Yes. (Says verbally or shakes head *yes*.)

Objective 3

When the clinician gives a 1-2 sentence verbal description of a target word/concept and gives the student two choices of answers, the student will verbally supply the correct answer with 80% accuracy.

Clinician: Listen, Pham. This is white and falls to the ground in flakes when it is very cold outside. Is it *wind* or *snow*?
Student: Snow.

Objective 4

When shown pictures of time/weather/season target vocabulary words, the student will give verbal, one-word labels with 80% accuracy.

Clinician: (Shows picture of *summer*.) Antoine, what season is this?
Student: Summer.

Objective 5

When asked to verbally list 3-5 items in a given category, the student will do so with 80% accuracy.

Clinician: Rosario, tell me the names of three seasons.
Student: Spring, summer, winter.

Objective 6

When asked to define a target vocabulary word, the student will give a 5+ word verbal description with 80% accuracy.

Clinician: Shaheda, what is a *calendar*?
Student: It is a chart with the months, days, and weeks of the year.

Objective 7

When given a time/weather/season target vocabulary word, the student will use the word in a sentence with 80% accuracy.

Clinician: Martak, please use the word *minute* in a sentence.
Student: A minute has 60 seconds.

For more advanced students: (written language)

Objective 8

When presented with a paragraph or word list containing the target vocabulary word, the student will find and read the word out loud with 80% accuracy.

Clinician: Giovan, look at this story. Please find the word *month*, and read the word to me after you find it.
Student: (Reads story.) Month. (Reads word aloud.)

Objective 9

When asked to spell a target vocabulary word, the student will spell the word out loud with 80% accuracy.

Clinician: Liam, please spell the word *winter*.
Student: (Spells the word out loud.)

Objective 10

When given a target vocabulary word, the student will write a sentence containing the word with 80% accuracy.

Clinician: Keenan, please write the word *week* in a sentence.
Student: (Writes a sentence containing the word *week*.)

Phonological Awareness Objectives

Annual Goal

Student will demonstrate increased phonological awareness skills.

Short-Term Objectives/Benchmarks

Objective 11 With 80% accuracy, the student will count the number of words in a sentence that is prewritten or that the student has written.

Clinician: Look, Stephan. Here is a sentence in our story. Count how many words are in that sentence.
Student: (Counts the number of words in the sentence.)

Clinician: Elijah, you wrote a good sentence using the word *cold*. Please count how many words are in your sentence.
Student: (Counts the number of words in the sentence.)

Objective 12 When given a target vocabulary word, the student will identify the number of syllables in that word with 80% accuracy.

Clinician: Cindy, how many syllables are in the word *minute*?
Student: Two.

Objective 13 When given a target vocabulary word, the student will identify the number of sounds in that word with 80% accuracy.

Clinician: Meuy, how many sounds are in the word *sun*?
Student: Three.

Objective 14 When the student hears a word that rhymes with a target vocabulary word, the student will identify that word verbally or nonverbally with 80% accuracy.

Clinician: Kosuke, color the picture that rhymes with *vain*.
Student: (Colors the picture of rain.)

Clinician: Dominique, what season rhymes with *thing*?
Student: Spring.

Objective 15

When the student hears the speech pathologist say a target vocabulary word phoneme by phoneme, that student will demonstrate sound blending skills by stating the whole word with 80% accuracy.

Clinician: Theresa, what word is this? /c/-/l/-/o/-/ck/
Student: Clock.

Objective 16

When given a target vocabulary word, the student will identify the first sound in that word upon request with 80% accuracy.

Clinician: Listen, Marcella. *Hot.* What's the first sound in that word?
Student: /h/

Objective 17

When given a target vocabulary word, the student will identify the last sound in that word upon request with 80% accuracy.

Clinician: Listen, Esperanza. *Wind.* What's the last sound in that word?
Student: /d/

Unit 6: Time, Weather, and Seasons

Target Words — Unit 6: Time, Weather, Seasons (+ Correct − Incorrect)	Objective 1 point to pictures Pretest Date	Posttest Date	Objective 2 yes/no Pretest Date	Posttest Date	Objective 3 2-choice answer Pretest Date	Posttest Date	Objective 4 1-word label Pretest Date	Posttest Date	Objective 5 list items Pretest Date	Posttest Date	Objective 6 verbal definition Pretest Date	Posttest Date
1. calendar												
2. clock												
3. cold												
4. day												
5. fall												
6. hot												
7. hour												
8. minute												
9. month												
10. night												
11. rain												
12. second												
13. snow												
14. spring												
15. summer												
16. sun												
17. week												
18. wind												
19. winter												
20. year												
% Correct	% Correct		% Correct		% Correct		% Correct		% Correct		% Correct	

The Source for Bilingual Students with Language Disorders

Unit 6: Time, Weather, and Seasons

Target Words Unit 6: Time, Weather, Seasons	Objective 7 say word in sentence		Objective 8 read word in paragraph		Objective 9 spell the word		Objective 10 write word in sentence		Objective 11 count words in sentence		Objective 12 count syllables in word	
+ Correct − Incorrect	Pretest Date	Posttest Date	Pretest Date	Posttest Date	Pretest Date	Posttest Date	Pretest Date	Posttest Date	Pretest Date	Posttest Date	Pretest Date	Posttest Date
1. calendar												
2. clock												
3. cold												
4. day												
5. fall												
6. hot												
7. hour												
8. minute												
9. month												
10. night												
11. rain												
12. second												
13. snow												
14. spring												
15. summer												
16. sun												
17. week												
18. wind												
19. winter												
20. year												
	% Correct	% Correct	% Correct	% Correct	% Correct	% Correct	% Correct	% Correct	% Correct	% Correct	% Correct	% Correct

Unit 6: Time, Weather, and Seasons

Target Words Unit 6: Time, Weather, Seasons + Correct − Incorrect	Objective 13 identify number of sounds in word Pretest Date / Posttest Date		Objective 14 identify rhyming word Pretest Date / Posttest Date		Objective 15 sound blending Pretest Date / Posttest Date		Objective 16 identify first sound in word Pretest Date / Posttest Date		Objective 17 identify last sound in word Pretest Date / Posttest Date	
1. calendar										
2. clock										
3. cold										
4. day										
5. fall										
6. hot										
7. hour										
8. minute										
9. month										
10. night										
11. rain										
12. second										
13. snow										
14. spring										
15. summer										
16. sun										
17. week										
18. wind										
19. winter										
20. year										
% Correct	% Correct	% Correct	% Correct	% Correct	% Correct	% Correct	% Correct	% Correct	% Correct	% Correct

Vocabulary Pictures: Cut these pictures apart to use in the activities that follow.

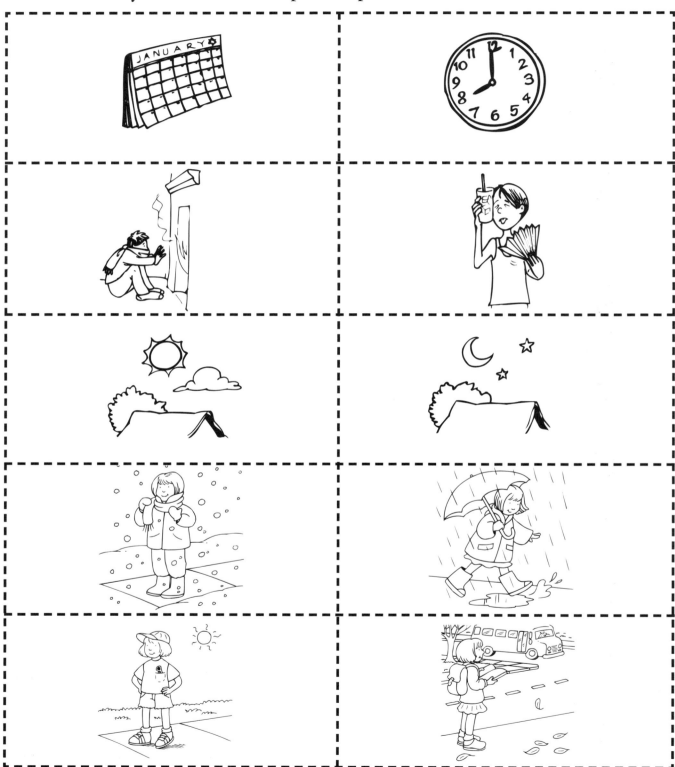

Vocabulary Pictures: Cut these pictures apart to use in the activities that follow.

There are many uses for these Word Cards, including having your students pair them with the picture cards, reading the words aloud (if students are able), or copying the words on the lines for practice. Use these vocabulary words in any way you see fit.

calendar	clock	cold
day	fall	hot
hour	minute	month
night	rain	second
snow	spring	summer
sun	week	wind
winter	year	

Vocabulary Word Definitions

calendar   A chart that has the months, weeks, and days of a year in it.

clock   An instrument for telling time. Usually it tells us what hour, minute, and second it is right now.

cold   A condition in which the temperature is low. We often feel this way in the winter.

day   A period of time lasting 24 hours. There are 7 of these in a week.

fall   The season after summer, when it starts getting cold and leaves fall off the trees.

hot   A condition in which the temperature is high. We often feel this way when the sun is shining in summer.

hour   A period of time lasting 60 minutes. There are 24 of these in one day.

minute   A period of time lasting 60 seconds. There are 60 of these in one hour.

month   A period of time lasting 4 weeks, or 30 days. There are 12 of these in one year.

night   A period of darkness during a day, when we see the moon and stars. We sleep at this time.

rain   Water that falls from clouds in the sky. It makes things wet.

second   A period of time that happens very fast. There are 60 of these in one minute.

snow   Frozen rain that falls in flakes from the sky. It is white and very cold.

spring   The season after winter, when plants start to grow again.

summer   The season after spring. It is the hottest season of the year.

sun   A source of light and heat. It is yellow and shines in the sky.

week   A period of time lasting 7 days. There are approximately 4 of these in each month.

wind   Air that is moving. We can't see it, but it blows and makes things like trees and leaves move.

winter   The season after fall. It is the coldest season of the year.

year   A period of time lasting 12 months, or 365 days.

Activity 1: Time, Weather, and Seasons

Have your students complete each definition with a word from the box. (Do this orally with nonreading students.)

winter	month	spring	day	night
hot	summer	cold	hour	fall

1. A _____ is a period of time lasting 24 hours. There are 7 of these in a week.

2. The _____ season is after spring. It is the hottest season of the year.

3. The _____ season is after summer, when it starts getting cold and leaves fall off the trees.

4. _____ is a period of darkness during the day, when we see the moon and stars. We sleep at this time.

5. A _____ is a period of time lasting 4 weeks, or about 30 days. There are 12 of these in one year.

6. The _____ season is after fall. It is the coldest season of the year.

7. An _____ is a period of time lasting 60 minutes. There are 24 of these in one day.

8. The _____ season is after winter, when plants start to grow again.

9. When it is _____, the temperature is high. We often feel this way when the sun is shining in summer.

10. When it is _____, the temperature is low. We often feel this way in the winter.

Activity 1: Time, Weather, and Seasons, *continued*

wind	year	week	calendar	second
minute	snow	clock	rain	sun

11. A _____ is an instrument for telling time. Usually it tells us what hour, minute, and second it is right now.

12. _____ is air that is moving. We can't see it, but it blows and makes things like trees and leaves move.

13. A _____ is a chart that has the months, weeks, and days of a year in it.

14. A _____ is a period of time lasting 12 months, or 365 days.

15. A _____ is a period of time lasting 60 seconds. There are 60 of these in one hour.

16. _____ is water that falls from clouds in the sky. It makes things wet.

17. A _____ is a period of time lasting 7 days. There are approximately 4 of these in each month.

18. A _____ is a period of time that happens very fast. There are 60 of these in one minute.

19. _____ is frozen rain that falls in flakes from the sky. It is white and very cold.

20. The _____ is a source of light and heat. It is yellow and shines in the sky.

Activity 2: Time, Weather, and Seasons

Holding up a picture of each item, have your students verbally supply the correct answer. (If students are advanced enough to read, they may circle the correct answers on their own.)

1. This is a period of darkness during the day, when we see the moon and stars. We sleep at this time.

   What is it?   **night**   **day**

2. This is a period of time lasting 4 weeks, or about 30 days. There are 12 of these in a year.

   What is it?   **minute**   **month**

3. This is a period of time lasting 24 hours. There are 7 of these in a week.

   What is it?   **day**   **week**

4. This season is after spring. It is the hottest season of the year.

   What is it?   **summer**   **winter**

5. This is air that is moving. We can't see it, but it blows and makes things like leaves and trees move.

   What is it?   **snow**   **wind**

6. This is a source of light and heat. It is yellow and shines in the sky.

   What is it?   **rain**   **sun**

7. This is a chart that has the months, weeks, and days of a year in it.

   What is it?   **calendar**   **clock**

8. This season is after summer, when it starts getting cold and leaves fall off the trees.

   What is it?   **fall**   **spring**

9. This is the season after fall. It is the coldest season of the year.

   What is it?   **winter**   **summer**

10. This is a condition in which the temperature is high. We often feel this way when the sun is shining in summer.

    What is it?   **hot**   **cold**

198

11. This is frozen rain that falls in flakes from the sky. It is white and very cold.

    What is it?   **sun**   **snow**

12. This is a period of time lasting 12 months, or 365 days.

    What is it?   **second**   **year**

13. This is a period of 7 days. There are approximately 4 of these in each month.

    What is it?   **week**   **hour**

14. This is a condition in which the temperature is low. We often feel this way in the winter.

    What is it?   **cold**   **hot**

15. This is a period of time that happens very fast. There are 60 of these in one minute.

    What is it?   **hour**   **second**

16. This is a period of time lasting 60 seconds. There are 60 of these in one hour.

    What is it?   **year**   **minute**

17. This is an instrument for telling time. Usually it tells us what hour, minute, and second it is right now.

    What is it?   **clock**   **calendar**

18. This is a period of time lasting 60 minutes. There are 24 of these in one day.

    What is it?   **hour**   **week**

19. This season is after winter, when plants start to grow again.

    What is it?   **spring**   **fall**

20. This is water that falls from clouds in the sky. It makes things wet.

    What is it?   **wind**   **rain**

Activity 3: Time, Weather, and Seasons

Have your student read the story. Ask him to find each vocabulary word and circle it as he reads. Your student can use the word cards on page 194 as a reference. The story contains all 20 vocabulary words.

Miguel was from the Philippines. He had just come to the States with his family. Miguel was in first grade, and he was learning lots of English. Miguel was also learning about seasons, time, and weather in the States.

In the Philippines, there were 2 seasons. Miguel learned that in the States, there are four seasons: winter, spring, summer, and fall. His teacher said that in winter, it is cold and there is rain and even snow in some places. The wind blows a lot in winter. In summer, it is usually hot and the sun shines on most days. The teacher said that summer is many people's favorite season because the days are long and nights are shorter.

Miguel also learned about the calendar and the clock. His teacher said that every year has 12 months, and each month has approximately 4 weeks. Miguel and his classmates learned to tell time on the clock. Miguel was excited about learning to tell time! He couldn't wait to tell his parents that he had learned that an hour has 60 minutes, and that each minute has 60 seconds. Miguel was learning a lot in his new class!

Optional Activities:

◆ Ask students to retell the story.
◆ Read the story out loud. Afterwards, ask questions about the story and have students provide answers. For example, "What did Miguel learn about the seasons? What did he learn about the calendar?"
◆ After reading the story out loud, pick target vocabulary words out of the story and say each word phoneme by phoneme to allow students to practice sound blending. Example: "/H/-/o/-/t/; what word is that?" (Objective 15)
◆ Pick out a sentence and ask a student to count the number of words in the sentence. (Objective 11)
◆ Have students read the story silently or out loud to practice reading skills.
◆ After students are familiar with the story, read it out loud and omit the target vocabulary words. Have the students orally fill in the blanks.

Activity 4: Time, Weather, and Seasons

Have your students complete these items to fulfill the listed objectives. Nonreading and nonwriting students can dictate the sentence while you transcribe it. (Objective 7)

1. Use the word *winter* in a sentence.

   _____

   _____

   How many words are in your sentence? _____
   How many syllables are in the word *winter*? _____
   How many sounds are in the word *winter*? _____

2. Use the word *spring* in a sentence.

   _____

   _____

   How many words are in your sentence? _____
   How many syllables are in the word *spring*? _____
   How many sounds are in the word *spring*? _____

3. Use the word *summer* in a sentence.

   _____

   _____

   How many words are in your sentence? _____
   How many syllables are in the word *summer*? _____
   How many sounds are in the word *summer*? _____

4. Use the word *fall* in a sentence.

   _____

   _____

   How many words are in your sentence? _____
   How many syllables are in the word *fall*? _____
   How many sounds are in the word *fall*? _____

5. Use the word *night* in a sentence.

   _____

   _____

   How many words are in your sentence? _____
   How many syllables are in the word *night*? _____
   How many sounds are in the word *night*? _____

Activity 4: Time, Weather, and Seasons, *continued*

6. Use the word *day* in a sentence.

   _____

   _____

         How many words are in your sentence?   _____

         How many syllables are in the word *day*?   _____

         How many sounds are in the word *day*?   _____

7. Use the word *month* in a sentence.

   _____

   _____

         How many words are in your sentence?   _____

         How many syllables are in the word *month*?   _____

         How many sounds are in the word *month*?   _____

8. Use the word *week* in a sentence.

   _____

   _____

         How many words are in your sentence?   _____

         How many syllables are in the word *week*?   _____

         How many sounds are in the word *week*?   _____

9. Use the word *year* in a sentence.

   _____

   _____

         How many words are in your sentence?   _____

         How many syllables are in the word *year*?   _____

         How many sounds are in the word *year*?   _____

10. Use the word *hour* in a sentence.

   _____

   _____

         How many words are in your sentence?   _____

         How many syllables are in the word *hour*?   _____

         How many sounds are in the word *hour*?   _____

11. Use the word *minute* in a sentence.

_____

_____

        How many words are in your sentence? _____

        How many syllables are in the word *minute*? _____

        How many sounds are in the word *minute*? _____

12. Use the word *second* in a sentence.

_____

_____

        How many words are in your sentence? _____

        How many syllables are in the word *second*? _____

        How many sounds are in the word *second*? _____

13. Use the word *calendar* in a sentence.

_____

_____

        How many words are in your sentence? _____

        How many syllables are in the word *calendar*? _____

        How many sounds are in the word *calendar*? _____

14. Use the word *rain* in a sentence.

_____

_____

        How many words are in your sentence? _____

        How many syllables are in the word *rain*? _____

        How many sounds are in the word *rain*? _____

15. Use the word *hot* in a sentence.

_____

_____

        How many words are in your sentence? _____

        How many syllables are in the word *hot*? _____

        How many sounds are in the word *hot*? _____

16. Use the word *cold* in a sentence.

_____

_____

      How many words are in your sentence?   _____

      How many syllables are in the word *cold*?   _____

      How many sounds are in the word *cold*?   _____

17. Use the word *clock* in a sentence.

_____

_____

      How many words are in your sentence?   _____

      How many syllables are in the word *clock*?   _____

      How many sounds are in the word *clock*?   _____

18. Use the word *snow* in a sentence.

_____

_____

      How many words are in your sentence?   _____

      How many syllables are in the word *snow*?   _____

      How many sounds are in the word *snow*?   _____

19. Use the word *wind* in a sentence.

_____

_____

      How many words are in your sentence?   _____

      How many syllables are in the word *wind*?   _____

      How many sounds are in the word *wind*?   _____

20. Use the word *sun* in a sentence.

_____

_____

      How many words are in your sentence?   _____

      How many syllables are in the word *sun*?   _____

      How many sounds are in the word *sun*?   _____

Activity 5: Time, Weather, and Seasons

Have your students complete these items to fulfill the listed objective. Tell the students that some of these are silly, made-up words.

1. Circle the one that rhymes with *blow*.

2. Circle the one that rhymes with *got*.

3. Circle the one that rhymes with *pecond*.

4. Circle the one that rhymes with *rear*.

5. Circle the one that rhymes with *lay*.

6. Circle the one that rhymes with *bummer*.

7. Circle the one that rhymes with *ring*.

8. Circle the one that rhymes with *fight*.

9. Circle the one that rhymes with *seek*.

10. Circle the one that rhymes with *ginute*.

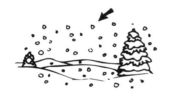

11. Circle the one that rhymes with *Spain*.

12. Circle the one that rhymes with *sock*.

13. Circle the one that rhymes with *fun*.

14. Circle the one that rhymes with *hinter*.

15. Circle the one that rhymes with *tall*.

16. Circle the one that rhymes with *funth*.

17. Circle the one that rhymes with *bower*.

18. Circle the one that rhymes with *malendar*.

19. Circle the one that rhymes with *sold*.

20. Circle the one that rhymes with *pinned*.

Activity 6: Time, Weather, and Seasons

Have your students complete these items to fulfill the listed objective.

Put an X on the picture when you hear its word said sound by sound. Say the word out loud.
(Example: /w/-/i/-/n/-/d/)

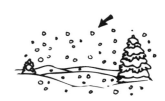

Activity 7: Time, Weather, and Seasons

Have your students complete these items to fulfill the listed objectives. Read each word and then ask a question. Record each student's responses in the lines provided.

1. **snow**

   What's the first sound in *snow*?   ——
   What's the last sound in *snow*?   ——
   How many syllables are in the word *snow*?   ——
   How many sounds are in the word *snow*?   ——

2. **clock**

   What's the first sound in *clock*?   ——
   What's the last sound in *clock*?   ——
   How many syllables are in the word *clock*?   ——
   How many sounds are in the word *clock*?   ——

3. **cold**

   What's the first sound in *cold*?   ——
   What's the last sound in *cold*?   ——
   How many syllables are in the word *cold*?   ——
   How many sounds are in the word *cold*?   ——

4. **wind**

   What's the first sound in *wind*?   ——
   What's the last sound in *wind*?   ——
   How many syllables are in the word *wind*?   ——
   How many sounds are in the word *wind*?   ——

5. **sun**

   What's the first sound in *sun*?   ——
   What's the last sound in *sun*?   ——
   How many syllables are in the word *sun*?   ——
   How many sounds are in the word *sun*?   ——

6. **calendar**

   What's the first sound in *calendar*?   ——
   What's the last sound in *calendar*?   ——
   How many syllables are in the word *calendar*?   ——
   How many sounds are in the word *calendar*?   ——

7. **rain**

   What's the first sound in *rain*? ____
   What's the last sound in *rain*? ____
   How many syllables are in the word *rain*? ____
   How many sounds are in the word *rain*? ____

8. **hot**

   What's the first sound in *hot*? ____
   What's the last sound in *hot*? ____
   How many syllables are in the word *hot*? ____
   How many sounds are in the word *hot*? ____

9. **hour**

   What's the first sound in *hour*? ____
   What's the last sound in *hour*? ____
   How many syllables are in the word *hour*? ____
   How many sounds are in the word *hour*? ____

10. **minute**

    What's the first sound in *minute*? ____
    What's the last sound in *minute*? ____
    How many syllables are in the word *minute*? ____
    How many sounds are in the word *minute*? ____

11. **second**

    What's the first sound in *second*? ____
    What's the last sound in *second*? ____
    How many syllables are in the word *second*? ____
    How many sounds are in the word *second*? ____

12. **month**

    What's the first sound in *month*? ____
    What's the last sound in *month*? ____
    How many syllables are in the word *month*? ____
    How many sounds are in the word *month*? ____

13. **week**

    What's the first sound in *week*? ____
    What's the last sound in *week*? ____
    How many syllables are in the word *week*? ____
    How many sounds are in the word *week*? ____

14. **year**

What's the first sound in *year*? _____
What's the last sound in *year*? _____
How many syllables are in the word *year*? _____
How many sounds are in the word *year*? _____

15. **fall**

What's the first sound in *fall*? _____
What's the last sound in *fall*? _____
How many syllables are in the word *fall*? _____
How many sounds are in the word *fall*? _____

16. **night**

What's the first sound in *night*? _____
What's the last sound in *night*? _____
How many syllables are in the word *night*? _____
How many sounds are in the word *night*? _____

17. **day**

What's the first sound in *day*? _____
What's the last sound in *day*? _____
How many syllables are in the word *day*? _____
How many sounds are in the word *day*? _____

18. **winter**

What's the first sound in *winter*? _____
What's the last sound in *winter*? _____
How many syllables are in the word *winter*? _____
How many sounds are in the word *winter*? _____

19. **spring**

What's the first sound in *spring*? _____
What's the last sound in *spring*? _____
How many syllables are in the word *spring*? _____
How many sounds are in the word *spring*? _____

20. **summer**

What's the first sound in *summer*? _____
What's the last sound in *summer*? _____
How many syllables are in the word *summer*? _____
How many sounds are in the word *summer*? _____

Vocabulary Objectives

Annual Goal — Student will demonstrate increased receptive and expressive vocabulary skills.

Short-Term Objectives/Benchmarks

Objective 1

When the clinician verbally gives safety/survival target vocabulary words, the student will point to pictures of these items with 80% accuracy.

Clinician: Guiseppe, point to *stop*. Point to *telephone*.
Student: (Points to each named picture.)

Objective 2

When the clinician holds up a picture and says, "Is this a(n) _____?" the student will verbally or nonverbally indicate *yes* or *no* with 80% accuracy.

Clinician: (Holds up a picture of *fire*.) Luisa, is this *poison*?
Student: No. (Says verbally or shakes head *no*.)

Clinician: (Holds up a picture of a *police officer*.) Arturo, is this a *police officer*?
Student: Yes. (Says verbally or shakes head *yes*.)

Objective 3

When the clinician gives a 1-2 sentence verbal description of a target word/concept and gives the student two choices of answers, the student will verbally supply the correct answer with 80% accuracy.

Clinician: Listen, Karen. This is a person who we don't know and don't talk to. We should be careful of this person. Is it a *stranger* or a *police officer*?
Student: Stranger.

Objective 4

When shown pictures of safety/survival target vocabulary words, the student will give verbal, one-word labels with 80% accuracy.

Clinician: (Shows picture of a *stop* sign.) Gunnar, what does this say?
Student: Stop.

Objective 5

When asked to verbally list 3-5 items in a given category, the student will do so with 80% accuracy.

Clinician: Janelle, tell me four important safety words.
Student: Danger, emergency, fire, warning.

Objective 6

When asked to define a safety/survival target vocabulary word, the student will give a 5+ word verbal description with 80% accuracy.

Clinician: Trina, what does *exit* mean?
Student: It means the place where you go out or leave.

Objective 7

When given a target vocabulary word, the student will use the word in a sentence with 80% accuracy.

Clinician: Alex, please use the word *help* in a sentence.
Student: If we need help, we can dial 911.

For more advanced students: (written language)

Objective 8

When presented with a paragraph or word list containing the target vocabulary word, the student will find and read the word out loud with 80% accuracy.

Clinician: Gina, look at this story. Please find the word *women*, and read the word to me after you find it.
Student: (Reads story.) Women. (Reads word aloud.)

Objective 9

When asked to spell a target vocabulary word, the student will spell the word out loud with 80% accuracy.

Clinician: Jon, please spell the word *entrance*.
Student: (Spells the word out loud.)

Objective 10

When given a target vocabulary safety/survival word, the student will write a sentence containing the word with 80% accuracy.

Clinician: Hanukah, please write the word *rest rooms* in a sentence.
Student: (Writes a sentence containing the word *rest rooms*.)

Phonological Awareness Objectives

Annual Goal   Student will demonstrate increased phonological awareness skills.

Short-Term Objectives/Benchmarks

Objective 11   With 80% accuracy, the student will count the number of words in a sentence that is prewritten or that the student has written.

> *Clinician:*   Look, Karl. Here is a sentence in our story. Count how many words are in that sentence.
>
> *Student:*   (Counts the number of words in the sentence.)

> *Clinician:*   Jarell, you wrote a good sentence using the word *closed*. Please count how many words are in your sentence.
>
> *Student:*   (Counts the number of words in the sentence.)

Objective 12   When given a target vocabulary word, the student will identify the number of syllables in that word with 80% accuracy.

> *Clinician:*   Rita, how many syllables are in the word *emergency*?
>
> *Student:*   Four.

Objective 13   When given a target vocabulary word, the student will identify the number of sounds in that word with 80% accuracy.

> *Clinician:*   Sophia, how many sounds are in the word *open*?
>
> *Student:*   Four.

Objective 14   When the student hears a word that rhymes with a target vocabulary word, the student will identify that word verbally or nonverbally with 80% accuracy.

> *Clinician:*   Kristofel, color the picture that rhymes with *manger*.
>
> *Student:*   (Colors the picture of the sign that says "Danger.")

> *Clinician:*   Caitlin, what safety word rhymes with *tire*?
>
> *Student:*   Fire.

Objective *15*

When the student hears the speech pathologist say a target vocabulary word phoneme by phoneme, that student will demonstrate sound blending skills by stating the whole word with 80% accuracy.

Clinician: Tasha, what word is this? /s/-/t/-/o/-/p/
Student: Stop.

Objective *16*

When given a target vocabulary word, the student will identify the first sound in that word upon request with 80% accuracy.

Clinician: Listen, Graciela. *Women*. What's the first sound in that word?
Student: /w/

Objective *17*

When given a target vocabulary word, the student will identify the last sound in that word upon request with 80% accuracy.

Clinician: Listen, Julio. *Help*. What's the last sound in that word?
Student: /p/

Unit 7: Safety and Survival

Target Words	Objective 1		Objective 2		Objective 3		Objective 4		Objective 5		Objective 6	
Unit 7: Safety and Survival	point to pictures		yes/no		2-choice answer		1-word label		list items		verbal definition	
+ Correct − Incorrect	Pretest Date	Posttest Date	Pretest Date	Posttest Date	Pretest Date	Posttest Date	Pretest Date	Posttest Date	Pretest Date	Posttest Date	Pretest Date	Posttest Date
1. ambulance												
2. caution												
3. closed												
4. danger												
5. emergency												
6. entrance												
7. exit												
8. fire												
9. help												
10. hot												
11. men												
12. open												
13. poison												
14. police officer												
15. private												
16. rest rooms												
17. stop												
18. stranger												
19. telephone												
20. women												
% Correct	Correct	% Correct	Correct	% Correct	Correct	% Correct	Correct	% Correct	Correct	% Correct	Correct	% Correct

Unit 7: Safety and Survival

Target Words	Objective 7 say word in sentence		Objective 8 read word in paragraph		Objective 9 spell the word		Objective 10 write word in sentence		Objective 11 count words in sentence		Objective 12 count syllables in word	
Unit 7: Safety and Survival	Pretest Date	Posttest Date	Pretest Date	Posttest Date	Pretest Date	Posttest Date	Pretest Date	Posttest Date	Pretest Date	Posttest Date	Pretest Date	Posttest Date
+ Correct − Incorrect												
1. ambulance												
2. caution												
3. closed												
4. danger												
5. emergency												
6. entrance												
7. exit												
8. fire												
9. help												
10. hot												
11. men												
12. open												
13. poison												
14. police officer												
15. private												
16. rest rooms												
17. stop												
18. stranger												
19. telephone												
20. women												
	% Correct	% Correct	% Correct	% Correct	% Correct	% Correct	% Correct	% Correct	% Correct	% Correct	% Correct	% Correct

Unit 7: Safety and Survival

Target Words	Objective 13 identify number of sounds in word		Objective 14 identify rhyming word		Objective 15 sound blending		Objective 16 identify first sound in word		Objective 17 identify last sound in word	
Unit 7: Safety and Survival	Pretest Date	Posttest Date	Pretest Date	Posttest Date	Pretest Date	Posttest Date	Pretest Date	Posttest Date	Pretest Date	Posttest Date
+ Correct − Incorrect										
1. ambulance										
2. caution										
3. closed										
4. danger										
5. emergency										
6. entrance										
7. exit										
8. fire										
9. help										
10. hot										
11. men										
12. open										
13. poison										
14. police officer										
15. private										
16. rest rooms										
17. stop										
18. stranger										
19. telephone										
20. women										
	% Correct	% Correct	% Correct	% Correct	% Correct	% Correct	% Correct	% Correct	% Correct	% Correct

Vocabulary Pictures: Cut these pictures apart to use in the activities that follow.

Vocabulary Pictures: Cut these pictures apart to use in the activities that follow.

There are many uses for these Word Cards, including having your students pair them with the picture cards, reading the words aloud (if students are able), or copying the words on the lines for practice. Use these vocabulary words in any way you see fit.

ambulance	caution	closed
danger	emergency	entrance
exit	fire	help
hot	men	open
poison	police officer	private
rest rooms	stop	stranger
telephone	women	

Vocabulary Word Definitions

ambulance   A special type of car or truck that has a siren and carries people who are sick or hurt.

caution   A word that means we need to be careful because something might hurt us. It means we should go slowly or even stop.

closed   A sign that means it's not OK to go inside.

danger   A sign that means something is bad for us, and we should stay away from it because it could hurt us.

emergency   When something happens quickly and suddenly. It means we have to do something right away.

entrance   A place like a door where we can go inside.

exit   A place like a door where we can leave or go out.

fire   A thing that is very hot and can burn us if we are not careful. It also keeps us warm when it's cold.

help   A word that a person says when they need someone to come right away and do something for them.

hot   A condition in which something can burn us or burn other things. We need to be careful around things like fire and stoves.

men   A word on a sign that means only men can go in there.

open   A word on a sign that means it's OK to go inside.

poison   Something that makes us sick and can even make us die. We should not touch it or eat it.

police officer   A person who helps keep people safe and helps them obey the law.

private   A word on a sign that means we can't go in there because it is only for certain people.

restrooms   A place where there are toilets that we can use.

stop   A word on a sign that means we should not move; we should be still.

stranger   A person we have never seen or met before. We should be careful about this kind of person.

telephone   A word on a sign that means there is something nearby that we can use to call someone.

women   A word on a sign that means only women can go in there.

Unit 7

Activity 1: Safety and Survival

Have your students complete each definition with a word from the box. (Do this orally with nonreading students.)

stop	caution	help	stranger	men
emergency	danger	entrance	exit	telephone

1. If a sign says _____, that means something is bad for us, and we should stay away from it because it could hurt us.

2. A _____ is a person we have never seen or met before. We should be careful about this kind of person

3. When a sign says _____, it means we should not move; we should be still.

4. An _____ is when something happens quickly and suddenly. It means we have to do something right away.

5. An _____ is a place like a door where we can leave or go out.

6. If a sign says _____, it means that only men can go in there.

7. _____ means that we need to be careful because something might hurt us. It means we should go slowly or even stop.

8. An _____ is a place like a door where we can go inside.

9. A sign that says _____ means that there is something nearby that we can use to call someone.

10. If a person says _____, it means they need someone to come right away and do something for them.

private	open	ambulance	women	poison
police officer	rest rooms	fire	hot	closed

11. If a sign says _____, it means that only women can go in there.

12. A sign that says _____ means that there is a place with toilets that we can use.

13. An _____ is a special type of car or truck that has a siren and carries people who are sick or hurt.

14. When something is _____, it can burn us or burn other things. We need to be careful around things like fire and stoves.

15. A sign that says _____ means that it's OK to go inside.

16. A _____ is a person who helps keep people safe and helps them obey the law.

17. _____ is very hot and can burn us if we are not careful. It also keeps us warm when it's cold.

18. _____ is something that makes us sick and can even make us die. We should not touch it or eat it.

19. A sign that says _____ means that we can't go in there because it is only for certain people.

20. A sign that says _____ means that it's not OK to go inside.

Activity 2: Safety and Survival

Holding up a picture of each item, have your students verbally supply the correct answer. (If students are advanced enough to read, they may circle the correct answers on their own.)

1. If a sign says this, it means that only men can go in there.

   What is it?   **open**   **men**

2. A sign that says this means that there are toilets we can use.

   What is it?   **rest rooms**   **ambulance**

3. This word means that we need to be careful because something might hurt us. It means we should go slowly or even stop.

   What is it?   **poison**   **caution**

4. This means a place like a door where we can go inside.

   What is it?   **entrance**   **fire**

5. This sign means that there is something nearby that we can use to call someone.

   What is it?   **stop**   **telephone**

6. If a person says this, it means they need someone to come right away and do something for them.

   What is it?   **help**   **private**

7. If a sign says this, it means something is bad for us, and we should stay away from it because it could hurt us.

   What is it?   **danger**   **open**

8. If a sign says this, it means that only women can go in there.

   What is it?   **police officer**   **women**

9. This is a special type of car or truck that has a siren and carries people who are sick or hurt.

   What is it?   **ambulance**   **exit**

10. This is very hot and can burn us if we are not careful. It also keeps us warm when it's cold.

    What is it?   **poison**   **fire**

11. This is when something happens quickly and suddenly. It means we have to do something right away.

    What is it?   **emergency**   **telephone**

12. This is something that makes us sick and can even make us die. We should not touch it or eat it.

    What is it?   **entrance**   **poison**

13. A sign that says this means that we can't go in there because it is only for certain people.

    What is it?   **private**   **men**

14. When something is like this, it can burn us or burn other things. We need to be careful around things like fire and stoves.

    What is it?   **exit**   **hot**

15. This is a person we have never seen or met before. We should be careful about this kind of person.

    Who is it?   **stranger**   **police officer**

16. When a sign says this, it means we should not move; we should be still.

    What is it?   **stop**   **open**

17. This is a place like a door where we can leave or go out.

    What is it?   **fire**   **exit**

18. A sign that says this means it's OK to go inside.

    What is it?   **open**   **danger**

19. This is a person who helps keep people safe and helps them obey the law.

    Who is it?   **stranger**   **police officer**

20. A sign that says this means it's not OK to go inside.

    What is it?   **closed**   **emergency**

Activity 3: Safety and Survival

Have your student read the story. Ask him to find each vocabulary word and circle it as he reads. Your student can use the word cards on page 222 as a reference. The story contains all 20 vocabulary words.

Officer Muñoz, a city police officer, came to Ms. Soldatenkov's third grade classroom to talk about safety. He told the children first that they should be careful if a stranger approached them. Officer Muñoz said that if a child felt like she was in danger, she should yell "Help!" and run away fast. Officer Muñoz reminded the class that they should always use caution if they do not know a person.

Officer Muñoz had brought some pictures with him to help the class learn safety words. He showed a picture of a fire which had started because something had gotten too hot. "A fire is an emergency," Officer Muñoz warned the class. "Sometimes an ambulance comes if people have been hurt." Officer Muñoz also talked about poison. "Be careful," he said, "because you could get sick or die if you touch or eat poison."

The next thing Officer Muñoz did was show the class some signs. The class knew that rest rooms meant that there was a toilet they could use, but that most rest rooms were marked men and women. They had to use the right rest room! They also had to make sure the rest rooms were open and that they were not marked private. The class and Officer Muñoz talked about how sometimes rest rooms were closed so people could not use them. Lastly, Officer Muñoz made sure the class could read the signs telephone, entrance, and exit. He also made sure that they could read the stop sign and know what it meant. Officer Muñoz taught the class a lot of things that day. Ms. Soldatenkov and the students were glad he had come!

Optional Activities:

◆ Ask students to retell the story.
◆ Read the story out loud. Afterwards, ask questions about the story and have students provide answers. For example, "Who came to the class? What kinds of things did this person talk about?"
◆ After reading the story out loud, pick target vocabulary words out of the story and say each word phoneme by phoneme to allow students to practice sound blending. Example: "/D/-/a/-/n/-/g/-/er/; what word is that?" (Objective 15)
◆ Pick out a sentence and ask a student to count the number of words in the sentence. (Objective 11)
◆ Have students read the story silently or out loud to practice reading skills.
◆ After students are familiar with the story, read it out loud and omit the target vocabulary words. Have the students orally fill in the blanks.

Activity 4: Safety and Survival

Have your students complete these items to fulfill the listed objectives. Nonreading and nonwriting students can dictate the sentence while you transcribe it. (Objective 7)

1. Use the words *police officer* in a sentence.

   _____

   _____

   How many words are in your sentence?   _____
   How many syllables are in the words *police officer*?   _____
   How many sounds are in the words *police officer*?   _____

2. Use the word *stop* in a sentence.

   _____

   _____

   How many words are in your sentence?   _____
   How many syllables are in the word *stop*?   _____
   How many sounds are in the word *stop*?   _____

3. Use the word *stranger* in a sentence.

   _____

   _____

   How many words are in your sentence?   _____
   How many syllables are in the word *stranger*?   _____
   How many sounds are in the word *stranger*?   _____

4. Use the word *exit* in a sentence.

   _____

   _____

   How many words are in your sentence?   _____
   How many syllables are in the word *exit*?   _____
   How many sounds are in the word *exit*?   _____

5. Use the word *caution* in a sentence.

   _____

   _____

   How many words are in your sentence?   _____
   How many syllables are in the word *caution*?   _____
   How many sounds are in the word *caution*?   _____

6. Use the words *rest rooms* in a sentence.

_____

_____

      How many words are in your sentence? _____

      How many syllables are in the word *rest rooms*? _____

      How many sounds are in the word *rest rooms*? _____

7. Use the word *closed* in a sentence.

_____

_____

      How many words are in your sentence? _____

      How many syllables are in the word *closed*? _____

      How many sounds are in the word *closed*? _____

8. Use the word *fire* in a sentence.

_____

_____

      How many words are in your sentence? _____

      How many syllables are in the word *fire*? _____

      How many sounds are in the word *fire*? _____

9. Use the word *emergency* in a sentence.

_____

_____

      How many words are in your sentence? _____

      How many syllables are in the word *emergency*? _____

      How many sounds are in the word *emergency*? _____

10. Use the word *hot* in a sentence.

_____

_____

      How many words are in your sentence? _____

      How many syllables are in the word *hot*? _____

      How many sounds are in the word *hot*? _____

11. Use the word *men* in a sentence.

_____

_____

          How many words are in your sentence?   _____

          How many syllables are in the word *men*?   _____

          How many sounds are in the word *men*?   _____

12. Use the word *telephone* in a sentence.

_____

_____

          How many words are in your sentence?   _____

          How many syllables are in the word *telephone*?   _____

          How many sounds are in the word *telephone*?   _____

13. Use the word *private* in a sentence.

_____

_____

          How many words are in your sentence?   _____

          How many syllables are in the word *private*?   _____

          How many sounds are in the word *private*?   _____

14. Use the word *ambulance* in a sentence.

_____

_____

          How many words are in your sentence?   _____

          How many syllables are in the word *ambulance*? _____

          How many sounds are in the word *ambulance*? _____

15. Use the word *poison* in a sentence.

_____

_____

          How many words are in your sentence?   _____

          How many syllables are in the word *poison*?   _____

          How many sounds are in the word *poison*?   _____

Activity 4: Safety and Survival, *continued*

16. Use the word *danger* in a sentence.

   _____

   _____

         How many words are in your sentence?   _____

         How many syllables are in the word *danger*?   _____

         How many sounds are in the word *danger*?   _____

17. Use the word *entrance* in a sentence.

   _____

   _____

         How many words are in your sentence?   _____

         How many syllables are in the word *entrance*?   _____

         How many sounds are in the word *entrance*?   _____

18. Use the word *women* in a sentence.

   _____

   _____

         How many words are in your sentence?   _____

         How many syllables are in the word *women*?   _____

         How many sounds are in the word *women*?   _____

19. Use the word *help* in a sentence.

   _____

   _____

         How many words are in your sentence?   _____

         How many syllables are in the word *help*?   _____

         How many sounds are in the word *help*?   _____

20. Use the word *open* in a sentence.

   _____

   _____

         How many words are in your sentence?   _____

         How many syllables are in the word *open*?   _____

         How many sounds are in the word *open*?   _____

Activity 5: Safety and Survival

Have your students complete these items to fulfill the listed objective. Tell the students that some of these are silly, made-up words.

1. Circle the one that rhymes with *ropen*.

2. Circle the one that rhymes with *yelp*.

3. Circle the one that rhymes with *simmon*.

4. Circle the one that rhymes with *bentrance*.

5. Circle the one that rhymes with *manger*.

6. Circle the one that rhymes with *toison*.

7. Circle the one that rhymes with *fambulance*.

8. Circle the one that rhymes with *kivate*.

9. Circle the one that rhymes with *relephone*.

10. Circle the one that rhymes with *den*.

11. Circle the one that rhymes with *got*.

12. Circle the one that rhymes with *zemergency*.

13. Circle the one that rhymes with *tire*.

14. Circle the one that rhymes with *jolice kofficer*.

15. Circle the one that rhymes with *hop*.

16. Circle the one that rhymes with *ranger*.

17. Circle the one that rhymes with *lexit*.

18. Circle the one that rhymes with *vaution*.

19. Circle the one that rhymes with *rest rooms*.

20. Circle the one that rhymes with *dozed*.

Activity 6: Safety and Survival

Have your students complete these items to fulfill the listed objective.

Put an X on the picture when you hear its word said sound by sound. Say the word out loud.
(Example: /h/-/o/-/t/)

Activity 7: Safety and Survival

Have your students complete these items to fulfill the listed objectives. Read each word and then ask a question. Record the students' responses in the lines provided.

1. **police officer**

   What's the first sound in *police*? _____
   What's the last sound in *police*? _____
   What's the first sound in *officer*? _____
   What's the last sound in *officer*? _____
   How many syllables are in the words *police officer*? _____
   How many sounds are in the words *police officer*? _____

2. **stop**

   What's the first sound in *stop*? _____
   What's the last sound in *stop*? _____
   How many syllables are in the word *stop*? _____
   How many sounds are in the word *stop*? _____

3. **stranger**

   What's the first sound in *stranger*? _____
   What's the last sound in *stranger*? _____
   How many syllables are in the word *stranger*? _____
   How many sounds are in the word *stranger*? _____

4. **exit**

   What's the first sound in *exit*? _____
   What's the last sound in *exit*? _____
   How many syllables are in the word *exit*? _____
   How many sounds are in the word *exit*? _____

5. **caution**

   What's the first sound in *caution*? _____
   What's the last sound in *caution*? _____
   How many syllables are in the word *caution*? _____
   How many sounds are in the word *caution*? _____

6. **restrooms**

   What's the first sound in *rest rooms*? _____
   What's the last sound in *rest rooms*? _____
   How many syllables are in the words *rest rooms*? _____
   How many sounds are in the words *rest rooms*? _____

Activity 7: Safety and Survival, *continued*

7. **closed**

   What's the first sound in *closed*? _____
   What's the last sound in *closed*? _____
   How many syllables are in the word *closed*? _____
   How many sounds are in the word *closed*? _____

   Sorry...we are
   CLOSED

8. **hot**

   What's the first sound in *hot*? _____
   What's the last sound in *hot*? _____
   How many syllables are in the word *hot*? _____
   How many sounds are in the word *hot*? _____

9. **fire**

   What's the first sound in *fire*? _____
   What's the last sound in *fire*? _____
   How many syllables are in the word *fire*? _____
   How many sounds are in the word *fire*? _____

10. **emergency**

    What's the first sound in *emergency*? _____
    What's the last sound in *emergency*? _____
    How many syllables are in the word *emergency*? _____
    How many sounds are in the word *emergency*? _____

11. **men**

    What's the first sound in *men*? _____
    What's the last sound in *men*? _____
    How many syllables are in the word *men*? _____
    How many sounds are in the word *men*? _____

12. **telephone**

    What's the first sound in *telephone*? _____
    What's the last sound in *telephone*? _____
    How many syllables are in the word *telephone*? _____
    How many sounds are in the word *telephone*? _____

13. **private**

    What's the first sound in *private*? _____
    What's the last sound in *private*? _____
    How many syllables are in the word *private*? _____
    How many sounds are in the word *private*? _____

    PRIVATE

14. **ambulance**

What's the first sound in *ambulance*? ____
What's the last sound in *ambulance*? ____
How many syllables are in the word *ambulance*? ____
How many sounds are in the word *ambulance*? ____

15. **poison**

What's the first sound in *poison*? ____
What's the last sound in *poison*? ____
How many syllables are in the word *poison*? ____
How many sounds are in the word *poison*? ____

16. **danger**

What's the first sound in *danger*? ____
What's the last sound in *danger*? ____
How many syllables are in the word *danger*? ____
How many sounds are in the word *danger*? ____

17. **entrance**

What's the first sound in *entrance*? ____
What's the last sound in *entrance*? ____
How many syllables are in the word *entrance*? ____
How many sounds are in the word *entrance*? ____

18. **women**

What's the first sound in *women*? ____
What's the last sound in *women*? ____
How many syllables are in the word *women*? ____
How many sounds are in the word *women*? ____

19. **help**

What's the first sound in *help*? ____
What's the last sound in *help*? ____
How many syllables are in the word *help*? ____
How many sounds are in the word *help*? ____

20. **open**

What's the first sound in *open*? ____
What's the last sound in *open*? ____
How many syllables are in the word *open*? ____
How many sounds are in the word *open*? ____

Asher, J.J. (1977). Learning another language through actions: The complete teacher's guide. Los Gatos, CA: Sky Oaks Productions.

Beaumont, C. (1992). Language intervention strategies for Hispanic LLD students. In H.W. Langdon with L.L. Cheng, *Hispanic children and adults with communication disorders: Assessment and intervention* (pp. 272-342). Gaithersburg, MD: Aspen Publishers, Inc.

Brice, A. & Roseberry-McKibbin, C. (1999). Turning frustration into success for English language learners. *Educational Leadership, 56* (7), 53-55.

Dodge, E.P. (2000). *The survival guide for school-based speech-language pathologists.* San Diego, CA: Singular Publishing Group/Thomson Learning.

Goldstein, B. (2000). *Cultural and linguistic diversity resource guide for speech-language pathologists.* San Diego, CA: Singular Publishing Group/ Thomson Learning.

Goldsworthy, C. (1998). *Sourcebook of phonological awareness activities: children's classic literature.* San Diego, CA: Singular Publishing Group/Thomson Learning.

Goldsworthy, C. (2001). *Sourcebook of phonological awareness activities: Children's core literature.* San Diego, CA: Singular Publishing Group/Thomson Learning.

Krashen, S.D. (1996). *Every person a reader: An alternative to the California Task Force Report on Reading.* Culver City, CA: Language Education Associates.

Mason, J. and Au, K. (1990). *Reading instruction for today.* (2nd ed.) Glenview, IL: Scott Foresman.

Ogle, D. (1986). A teaching model that develops active reading of expository text. *The Reading Teacher,* 39, 564-570.

Peregoy, S.F. and Boyle, O.W. (1997). *Reading, writing, and learning in ESL: A resource book for K-12 teachers.* (2nd ed.) New York: Longman Publishers, USA.

Richards, J.C. and Rodgers, T.S. (1986). *Approaches and methods in language teaching: A description and analysis.* New York: Cambridge University Press.

Robertson, C. and Salter, W. (1997). *The Phonological Awareness Book— Intermediate.* East Moline, IL: LinguiSystems, Inc.

References, *continued*

Roseberry-McKibbin, C. (1995). *Multicultural students with special language needs: Practical strategies for assessment and intervention.* Oceanside, CA: Academic Communication Associates.

Roseberry-McKibbin, C. and Hegde, M.N. (2000). *An advanced review of speech-language pathology: Preparation for NESPA and comprehensive examination.* Austin, TX: Pro-Ed.

Tabors, P.O. (1997). *One child, two languages: A guide for preschool educators of children learning English as a second language.* Baltimore, MD: Paul H. Brookes Publishing Co.

Terrell, T. (1992). The natural approach in bilingual education. In D.P. Dolson (Ed.), *Schooling and language minority students: A theoretical framework.* (pp. 117-146). Los Angeles: Evaluation, Dissemination and Assessment Center, California State University, Los Angeles, CA.

Trelease, J. (1995). *The read-aloud handbook.* New York: Penguin.

Ventriglia, L. (1982). *Conversations of Miguel and Maria: How children learn a second language.* Philippines: Addison-Wesley Publishing Company, Inc.

23-07-9876